COUNTRY FOXES

COUNTRY FOXES

Hugh Kolb

with illustrations by DIANA E. BROWN

Whittet Books

British Library Cataloguing in Publication Data. A catalogue record for this book is available from the British Library.

ISBN 1 873580 29 0

Printed and bound in Britain by
Biddles Ltd, Guildford and King's Lynn

Contents

Why aren't foxes dogs?

In one sense they are, because they both belong to the same mammalian family, the *Canidae*. These have common features which distinguish them from the other main mammalian Carnivores, such as bears, raccoons, mongooses, hyaenas, cats, weasels and seals. The Canids are small to medium-sized generalised carnivores which appeared early on in mammalian evolution (around 40 million years ago) and have remained more or less unchanged to the present day. Although the different species vary in things like overall size or the relative length of the ears and tail, none is far from what most people would recognise as a dog-like form. While there are a number of other obscure fox or dog like animals around the world, the Canids can be divided into three principal types:

- The true dogs, such as wolves, jackals and the domesticated dog
- The South American foxes, which are of an intermediate character and have sometimes been called fox/dogs
- The true foxes. Of these, the red fox is the commonest and most widespread species and the one that we are interested in

The dogs and foxes are distinguished from other mammalian carnivores mainly by their running ability and tooth form.

The original mammal foot pattern has five toes. The dogs and foxes are specialised to the extent that one of the toes has been lost on the hind limb, and remains only as a vestigial dew claw high up on the front limb. They stand up on the remaining four, as opposed to squatting on their heels like bears and weasels. The extension of the wrist and ankle bones (the carpals and tarsals) makes each limb longer and gives a greater pivotal length which improves running ability. This sort of evolutionary trend has been carried to extremes in herbivores like the horses and antelopes. There the toes have been reduced to one and two in number respectively in order to give maximum stability and leverage for pure running. This is so that they can escape from carnivores. Cats also have their foot bones extended to some degree, but the hind limbs are rather more developed than the front so that they can sprint and spring onto their prey. Dogs are more concerned with tracking and running down prey over longer distances.

The form and number of teeth are very important in distinguishing between the different types of mammals. On the one hand they reflect the

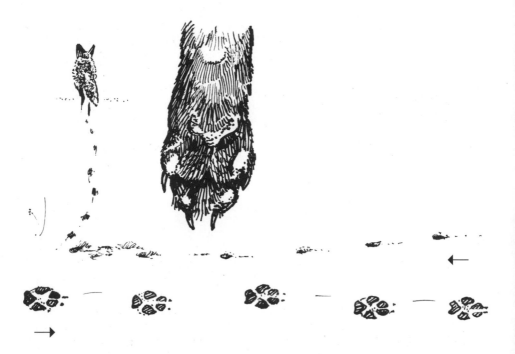

Fox paw pad and footprints.

major specialisations in diet between groups, i.e. cutting and biting as opposed to grinding and chewing. They are also the hardest parts of the body and are more likely to be preserved as fossils. They therefore provide much of the basic information that has been used to classify mammals and describe their evolution.

The tooth arrangement of the red fox is typical of canids and is often summarised by a 'dental formula', which for the fox is:

$$\text{I: } \frac{3}{3} \qquad \text{C: } \frac{1}{1} \qquad \text{P: } \frac{4}{4} \qquad \text{M: } \frac{2}{3}$$

This is a description of the number of teeth in one side of the upper and lower jaw. Starting out at the left (and front) there are 3 incisors (I) above, which provide a nibbling and pulling action. Next follow an upper and lower canine (C), the long pointed teeth (à la Dracula) which are the main strike force of the jaw. Behind are four upper and lower premolars (P).

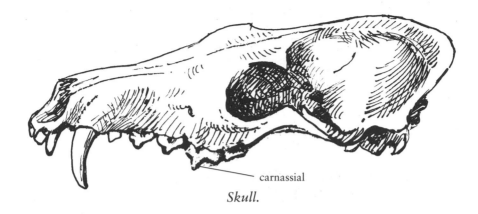

carnassial

Skull.

These are generalised gripping teeth, except for the last upper premolar which has evolved into a large upper carnassial. This, together with the similarly enlarged first lower molar (M), is the main cutting equipment of the jaw. The upper carnassial has a large point with a flat inner face which shears down alongside the outer face of the lower carnassial. This, and the fact that they are near the jaw hinge where the main chewing muscles are inserted, enables them to exert the power required for cutting up meat and cracking bones. The remaining molars are flattened and used for chewing and crushing. The last lower molar in the red fox is very small and almost vestigial. It is in fact missing completely in about a quarter of all foxes. Nobody knows why or whether this is of any significance. It is probably a simple inherited characteristic in fox populations and may be a stage in the evolution of a reduced tooth row.

Typically, therefore, foxes and dogs have 42 teeth, which is quite a lot. Among the better known mammals only moles and pigs have more. Cats,

Lower jaw, seen from inside, with some of the jaw bone removed.

carnassial

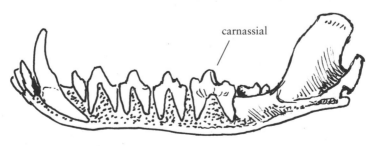

for instance, only have 30 teeth and the canines and carnassials are more highly developed and specialised for gripping and shearing. Fossil evidence suggests that the original primitive condition in mammals is to have 44 teeth, which shows how close the *Canidae* are to the basic mammalian form.

Fox names

Vulpes   The Latin word for a fox. Medieval bestiaries give the origin of the name as coming from *volupes*, meaning 'twisty foot'. This refers to the opinion that the fox had devious habits and never ran in a straight line when chased. Linnaeus (1707-1778, a Swedish naturalist whose real name was Karl von Linné) used it in his 'binomial nomenclature'. This was part of a system he devised for the classification of animals and plants. It uses Latinised words in structures which reflect the relationship of species. He called the fox *Vulpes vulpes*, the first name being the genus and the second the species name (in this case there are around ten species). They are both the same because this was the first species in the genus to be described (an accident of geography since this is the commonest fox in Sweden). The modern scientific name of the fox is in fact *Vulpes vulpes* L. The capital L. has been added as a convention to show that it was Linnaeus himself who made the first description. If Linnaeus had chosen Greek instead of Latin for his system, the fox would have been called $A\lambda\omega\pi\eta\xi$ $\alpha\lambda\omega\pi\eta\xi$. In Romanised characters this is *Alopex* which he used as part of the Latin name for the Arctic fox (confusing, isn't it?).

Fox   The common English name, more precisely known as the red fox to distinguish it from other species. It is Germanic in origin (old German – *Fuhs*; modern German – *Fuchs*).

Skulk   The collective noun for a group of foxes. This was probably invented by somebody who wanted to complete a list. Anybody who finds a sensible use for it is eligible for a prize.

Vixen   The name for a female fox. Although it doesn't look like it at first this has a similar Germanic origin as fox (old German – *Fuhsin*; modern German – *Füchsin*).

Tod   A common Scottish and North of England term for a fox. The origin is unknown.

Reynard   A name sometimes used for foxes which derives from the medieval poem *Reynard the Fox*. This was so popular in France as *Le Roman de Renard*, or *Renard le Goupil* , that 'renard' entered the language as the word for fox, replacing 'goupil'.

Charlie   A nickname which is popular in English sporting circles. It is derived from Charles James Fox (1749-1806), who was an English liberal politician and the first British Foreign Secretary. He was sympathetic to the French Revolution and in favour of legislation to limit the powers of the monarchy (the king at the time being George III – the one who talked to trees). The landowning and hunting classes transferred the name satirically to their favourite prey.

Llwynog   The Welsh for fox.

Sionnach   Fox in Scots Gaelic.

Shynnagh   The Manx word for a fox (although since we are led to believe that there aren't any foxes on the Isle of Man – either with or without tails – this seems redundant).

So what is a fox?

Most people, if asked to describe a fox, could come up with the salient vulpine features fairly quickly. They would include small size, a pointed snout, large ears and (most important of all) a long bushy tail. The more interesting question, though, is, 'Why should foxes look like that?'

Nowadays most biologists have an implicit faith in Charles Darwin's theory of evolution by natural selection. They believe that over millions of years, inherited changes that by chance made a species better fitted to survive have accumulated so that what we see now is the form best adapted to fufil its particular role in nature. When I was an undergraduate one of our lecturers used to stomp up and down in front of the class, going red in the face, trying to convince us that all the body forms and behaviours that could be seen in the animal kingdom were the result of adaption through natural selection. If we didn't understand how this had happened in a particular instance, then it was just due to our lack of imagination. Other less imaginative but more rigorous characters have sometimes criticised this sort of evolutionary biology as consisting of a lot of 'Just So' stories ('How The Elephant Got Its Trunk', etc). This is not to say that there isn't a large body of observation and experiment which is consistent with Darwin's theory, but it covers a small fraction of the species that have been described. Many studies have depended upon looking in a broad way at a number of related species, analysing aspects of feeding and environment which are different between them, and then seeing if there is a correlation between these and differences in form or behaviour. The problem in applying this to foxes is that most of these adaptions are supposed to have taken place many millions of years ago. Since catholicity of tastes and adaptability of habits can almost be considered characteristic of many canid species, it may be difficult to sort out which features are important. Urban foxes, for instance, are no longer living in conditions that resemble those where the species originally evolved. There weren't any back gardens in Dulwich 8 million years ago! However, we can go through the main points of a fox in order and see what they suggest about its niche in the world.

Foxes are quite slightly built animals. When seen skinned or in the summer after moulting they look thin and not overfed. The same fox seen during the middle of winter, however, seems to have doubled its size. This increase doesn't come from fat – which, when it is put on, is nearly all in the body cavity – but from the growth of a thick, spiky fur coat. In fact of

jackal

bat-eared fox

red fox

Arctic fox

winter coat

summer coat

fennec fox

wolf

all the fox species the red fox is the largest. The smallest is the fennec fox from North Africa which is about 20 centimetres (8 inches) high at the shoulder and weighs around 1.5 kg (3.3 lb). Even the red fox is small compared to some of the dog species, like the timber wolf and the African hunting dog. Furthermore, these hunt in packs, making them formidable predators, whereas the fox hunts alone. This suggests that foxes are not designed to tackle large prey, even when it doesn't fight back. Faced with an inviting sheep carcass badgers can make a meal of it in short order, whereas a fox spends a long time just trying to break into the juiciest parts. Even a small working terrier has a much stronger bite than a fox and in close encounters underground is quite capable of breaking a fox's lower jaw. Foxes, therefore, are best equipped to deal with prey much smaller than themselves. In a modern agricultural landscape this can include a great variety of things (which will be dealt with in a later chapter on food) but in the past when foxes evolved a much greater proportion of their diet probably consisted of small rodents.

While the red fox has distinctive pointy ears, they are not exceptional. Some of the smaller species, particularly those living in desert areas, such as the fennec fox, have enormous ears relative to their body size. One explanation suggested for this is that animals living in high temperatures need appendages, such as ears, with a large surface area in order to radiate

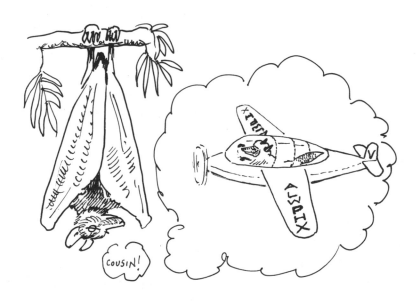

COUSIN!

The parts of a fox.

heat from the body. Arctic foxes, in contrast, have short, stubby ears which are nearly hidden in their fur. One of the older adages of descriptive biology is Allen's Rule (named after an American biologist) which states that items that stick out from the body become smaller as you go further north in order to conserve heat. Whether this is the case or not, ears still serve their main function of hearing. A largely nocturnal carnivore that hunts rodents, many of which are in runs or under clumps of grass, needs to be able to focus sound accurately before pouncing. Rodents produce many sounds, particularly distress calls, which are ultrasonic. Foxes have an upper threshold of hearing at 65,000 Hz (the upper limit of human hearing is about 20,000 Hz) and are capable of hearing these, supposedly up to 50 metres (164 feet) away. In some circumstances hearing may be more important than smell for hunting success.

The single most distinctive feature of a fox which everybody knows about is its tail or 'brush'. Like ears, tails may serve several functions at the same time. In many mammals, such as primates and squirrels, long tails are a necessity for balance and allow them to jump and climb securely. Foxes are in fact quite good at climbing. Urban foxes scale and run along walls as part of their normal routine. There are occasional records of foxes denning in trees, sometimes in hollowed out old willows or in the thickets of secondary shoots that surround the boles of old lime trees. The

American gray fox is noted as a climber and is as likely to go up a tree to escape pursuit as it is to go to ground. There used to be a pair in Regents Park Zoo in London which could be seen from above, curled up asleep in the topmost branches of a small tree. However we are not used to seeing our foxes bounding from tree to tree like squirrels. Desert and tundra living foxes have brushes but not much access to trees, so where climbing occurs it is probably a secondary development. When catching rodents foxes have a characteristic high leap which enables them to come down directly from above and trap the prey with their forepaws. The tail may provide some stability during this manoeuvre but none of these explanations sheds light on why it is so hairy.

The main function of hair in mammals is insulation, since they are characteristically warm blooded. However, another use that hair has been put to is to provide a large surface area for spreading smells from adjacent scent glands. In relatively hairless mammals like ourselves this is almost its sole function, as demonstrated by the hair in our armpits and other areas that we won't go into (at least not at the moment). These hair patches are

Gray fox up tree and red fox on ground.

associated with scent glands and a similar situation occurs in foxes. Two of the main sets of scent glands in the fox are above the anus, just underneath the tail (the anal glands), and on the upper surface of the tail (the supracaudal or 'violet' gland – apparently so called because the person who first described it thought it smelt of violets).

Anybody who has been closely associated with a fox will know that they are particularly smelly (the foxes that is – well maybe). One of the disadvantages we have as humans in studying other mammals is that much of their communication is conducted via smells, a sense in which we are not very acute. So if a fox seems smelly to us, with their much more highly developed olfactory ability think how it must seem to another fox! While similar glands occur in all canids, in sociable dogs like the wolf they are much reduced. Dogs rely to some extent on close contact, with visual and vocal signals for communication, whereas in the more solitary, nocturnal foxes scent is probably more important. This is not to say that foxes are completely quiet, as anybody who has been near a screaming vixen in the middle of the night will attest, but they use sounds in a much more limited way. Just as an example, if you accidentally tread on a dog's foot, everybody in the block knows about it, whereas an adult fox in a snare or trap, in any level of extremis, is totally silent. As a pack animal the dog feels impelled to communicate its distress to the other dogs around it, either to warn them or to seek help. The fox, by contrast, keeps its problems to itself, even though, subjectively, we must assume that its feelings are the same. With a different social behaviour it has shifted the balance of its communications with other members of the same species towards smells. A fox's brush may therefore be literally that: a means of enhancing the spread of socially important smells and leaving a strong trail to attract or warn off other foxes which appear on the scene some time after the resident has passed. Indeed the ability to leave such a trail was one of the reasons that drew our hunting forefathers so much to the fox.

Much of the above discussion is speculative, as is the way with 'Just So' stories. But it provides an understandable context into which to place the fox. We can see it as a small, solitary, nocturnal, rodent-hunting carnivore that relies on scent for communication. This is inevitably a simplification, and subsequent chapters will show that the fox's adaptability has enabled it to exploit a wide range of circumstances. However it should be remembered that much of the fox's present environment is artificial, and many of the competing species of carnivores that would have originally been there to restrict the fox to its own niche have been reduced or exterminated.

Personalities

In addition to its biological *raison d'être,* the fox has been equipped with parallel personalities by the people that it has lived amongst. It first entered the mainstream of European literary consciousness in the *Fables of Aesop.* Aesop is supposed to have been a Phrygian slave who lived around 500 BC (Phrygia was an area of Asia Minor, currently part of north-east Turkey). He was freed because of his story-telling abilities and his fables were subsequently collected and published in the 1st century AD by other classical writers. In fact *Aesop's Fables* are a distillation of folk law and didactic tales from the whole of classical Europe and the Middle East. Attributing human capacities to animals probably derives from older animist traditions, common to people everywhere. It is easy to see aspects of human personality in the characteristic behaviour of some familiar species

The Fox and the Crane.

and these are used to 'personify' the animals. These ideas can be used in stories to highlight human personality traits, or even in beliefs that the animals are real people who have been transformed, either by reincarnation or through shape-shifting (but not as we know it, Jim).

The foxes in Aesop are all fairly rational and not particularly malicious. In a representative recent translation there are 244 fables. A fox is the chief protagonist in 9 of these and appears as a major player in another 8. While chicken theft and hunting come into 4 of them, in most the fox is either a solver of problems or a clever beneficiary of others' misfortune. In some the fox is entirely neutral and just passes philosophical reflections on life's problems.

Until recently, study of the classics was considered the basis of any education in Europe, so that *Aesop's Fables* were always available as a source for contemplation and modification. During the Middle Ages beast epics were a popular form of literature. However the rational and intellectual climate of Greece and Rome had been replaced by the more broad brush guilt complex of medieval Christianity, so the characters and morals became less urbane and more pointed. The most famous of these epics was the story of *Reynard the Fox*. This was popular in France and the Nether-lands from the 12th century onwards. By the late 15th century it had been published in Antwerp as a poem running to nearly 8,000 lines and the text in one form or another had been spread throughout Europe. The name Reynard entered the common speech of many countries. His wife, Dame Hermelin, didn't manage to make it to posterity, but one of his sons, Russel, fared better. Reynard himself was the original anti-hero, sly, amoral, cow-ardly and self-seeking, but at the same time possessing an admirable cunning that was needed for survival. The poem tells of events at the court of King Noble, a lion. All the other animals, led by Isengrim the Wolf, band to-gether and complain to the king about the injuries and thefts that Reynard has inflicted on them. The king summons the fox to court. Initially he refuses to turn up but eventually appears and is put on trial. Reynard manages to argue his way out of the charges and promises to repent. The king pardons him and gives him His protection, under which Reynard takes revenge on those who accused him, particularly the wolf. The main purpose of the story is to satirise the moral and spiritual shortcomings of society using animals instead of people.

The best known fox poem in English of the same period is Chaucer's 'Nun's Priests Tale'. This is mainly a retelling of Aesop's Fox and Cock Fable, from the point of view of the cock, with European undertones de-rived from Reynard the Fox. The cock has a terrible dream of something large and hairy which is going to attack him, and according to plan a fox turns up one night and, after killing some of his hens, grabs him by the neck and runs off. The local people run after him and the cock says to the fox, 'Tell them I belong to you anyway and to mind their own business.' When the fox opens his mouth to speak the cock escapes, flies up into the nearest tree and gives him a raspberry,

> 'Nay,' quod the fox, 'but God yeve him meschaunce,
> That is so indiscreet of governaunce,
> The Iangleth whan he sholde holde his pees.'

in which there is a lesson for us all. The European origins of Chaucer's story are suggested by the line 'A col-fox, full of sly iniquitee'. The words 'col-fox' have been interpreted as meaning a coal, black or brandt fox, which is now called a 'cross fox' in English. This is a colour variety of the red fox which is rare in Britain (at least nowadays) but commoner in north-ern and central Europe.

The Fox's Tale

A fox is carelessly going about its business one night when it wanders into a rather vicious trap. However, instead of killing it, the trap just manages to chop the fox's tail off. After recovering from the injury the fox decides that this is a rather embarrassing predicament to be in. For a while it hides from other foxes because it doesn't want to be discriminated against for being different. Eventually this makes life even more difficult so it calls together all the other foxes for a meeting. 'Look at me!' fox says, 'Once I was the same as you, with that monstrous appendage that you're all dragging around so mindlessly. But then I had an inspiration! Why not get rid of such a useless and ugly thing? Now, see the change! How much better I look and feel! I urge you all to follow my example. If you don't you will never know how much more fulfilling life can be without a tail.'

Moral: *the advice you receive from others may not be disinterested* (caveat emptor – *let the buyer beware!*).

The Fox and the Mask

One day a fox wandered into an actor's dressing room (an unlikely occurrence one would have thought, but maybe thespians in ancient Greece lived in more rural surroundings than those of today – either that or this was an ancestor of one of today's urban foxes). The fox rummaged among the actor's properties and found a mask which impressed him (or her) a great deal for the handsomeness of its profile (whether this is because it looked more like a fox than a human, we are not told). Looking behind the mask all that the fox found was an empty space. 'Ah!' said the fox, 'such a fine head, but it has no brains!'

Moral: *the world has never been short of simplistic and patronising stories.*

Both of these from Aesop (with apologies)

The Fox and Duck

A Fox and a Duck, having quarrelled about the ownership of a frog, referred the matter to a Lion. After hearing a deal of argument the Lion opened his mouth to deliver judgement. 'I know what your decision is,' said the Duck, interrupting. 'It is that by your own showing the frog belongs to neither of us, and you will eat him yourself. Permit me to say that this is unjust, as I shall prove.' 'To me,' said the Fox, 'it is clear that you will give the frog to the Duck and the Duck to me and take me yourself. I am not without experience of the law.' 'I was about to explain,' said the Lion, yawning, 'that during the arguments in this case the property in dispute has hopped away. Perhaps you can procure another frog.'

Ambrose Bierce Fantastic Fables

The Fox and Grapes

A Fox, seeing some sour grapes hanging within an inch of his nose, and being unwilling to admit that there was anything he would not eat, solemnly declared that they were out of his reach.

Ambrose Bierce Aesopus Emendatus

The Farmer and Fox

A Farmer who had a deadly hatred against a certain Fox caught him and tied some tow to his tail; then carrying him to the centre of his own grain-field, he set the tow on fire and let the animal go. 'Alas!' said the farmer, seeing the result; 'if that grain had not been heavily insured I might have had to dissemble my hatred of the Fox.'

Ambrose Bierce Aesopus Emendatus

Where and why?

The red fox is naturally distributed right around the Northern Hemisphere. It is found from the deserts of central Asia up to the Siberian tundra. However at these extremes of its range it is in competition with the smaller desert foxes in the south and the Arctic fox in the north. In between, in the Boreal region, it is the commonest middle sized carnivore. While this kind of forested area may have been the fox's original habitat, its present distribution has been strongly influenced by human activities. On the one hand the fox is small and secretive enough to survive close to human habitation and to exploit the varied by-products of agriculture and urbanisation. On the other, the pervasive effects of the British Empire's sporting obsessions have led to the fox being introduced into places where it would not otherwise have occurred. The chief of these is Australia where foxes were released for hunting during the latter part of the last century. Over the next fifty years they spread to most parts of the continent apart from the central desert and the tropical north. This was in part associated with the explosive spread of the similarly introduced European rabbit, but also at the expense of the native marsupial fauna. The red fox in North America was in the past classified as a separate species *Vulpes fulva*, but is now considered to be the same as the European fox. It was mainly found in the northern forested areas. To the south, European foxes were introduced for hunting because the commonest local type, the gray fox, refuses to run and often hides in the trees when chased. The new foxes became established on farmland and eventually met up with and presumably interbred with the locals whose forested habitat was being depleted by logging. Their offspring followed the spread of agriculture and now red foxes are found over most of the USA and Canada. Foxes have also been moved around within Europe. It used to be common for cubs or bag foxes to be shipped south from Scotland, where they were considered a pest, to the Home Counties to increase the local stock which had been depleted by overhunting or disease. There are also records of Swedish animals being imported into England by hunts possibly, because they are larger, to try and increase the stamina of the local population.

At one time the British Isles had a full complement of predators – wolves, bears, lynx, wildcats and polecats – in addition to the fox. The lynx may have died out in prehistoric times, but the rest were either exterminated or their populations reduced to a remnant by predator control. Even the fox,

one of nature's great survivors, must have found it hard going at times. It is probable that if it weren't for the popularity of mounted hunts in central and southern England during the last two hundred years, foxes would be less numerous now than they are. They are presently found in all parts of mainland Britain but this probably only re-establishes the position in the distant past. With the rise of sheep farming and game preservation strenuous efforts were made in some parts of the country to reduce all predators. Foxes were all but eliminated over large parts of East Anglia and the lowland areas of north-east Scotland, partly also as a by-product of the rabbit trapping industry. The use of gin traps set in the open not only caught rabbits for market but also disposed of anything else that might interfere with trade. Fox numbers started to recover from about 1950 onwards. In a bounty scheme for fox tails in north-east Scotland only 54 out of 123 parishes returned foxes in 1960, whereas by 1970 only six parishes didn't produce foxes. On the coast, the Sands of Forvie nature reserve had had little fox trouble for many years but after 1970 predation on nesting eider ducks and terns became a problem.

The pressure on foxes was most noticeable in places where there was a geographical barrier to dispersal such as peninsulars and islands. They were exterminated from places like the Lleyn Peninsula of Caernarvonshire, parts of Pembrokeshire, Kintyre, the Black Isle and the Nigg Peninsular in

Ross and Cromarty. Their reappearance in some of these places has been recorded. For instance foxes were first caught again on the Black Isle in 1962, disappeared for a few years and reinvaded in strength in 1966. The last fox on Mull was killed in the 17th century and they died out on Anglesey in the late 1900s but were reintroduced in the 1960s. They survive on the Isle of Wight and Skye but the other main islands such as the Isle of Man, most of the Inner and Outer Hebrides, and Orkney and Shetland are too far away from the mainland ever to have had a fox population.

The other change in distribution that has occurred in recent years is the appearance of urban foxes. These first became apparent in the suburbs of London in the 1950s, but they are now known to be present in nearly all the bigger cities in the UK. It could be argued in many cases that the foxes did not move into cities but that the cities moved out to include them. However you look at it, they have found towns ideally suited to their needs and the density of foxes in some cities such as Bristol is now greater than in most rural areas.

Size and shape

In recent years, with the introduction of ginormous computers, fiercely hard mathematical techniques, and a better understanding of the way in which inherited characters are distributed in wild populations, taxonomists have tried to put the classification of animals on an objective basis (taxonomy is the science of classification). In the past many of the decisions about what constituted a genus, a species or a subspecies were based on the subjective opinions and personal quirks of individual biologists. It is almost inevitable that, faced with 99 specimens that all look the same and one that looks odd, people tend to be interested in the odd one. In fact, from the point of view of making general statements, it is the 99 that should be focused on. Taxonomists used to be regarded as falling into two broad camps, the 'lumpers' and the 'splitters'. Lumpers tended to take a broad, phlegmatic view of populations and were prepared to accept that natural variability between animals in any one place is liable to throw up a few extreme types. Splitters tended to regard each slightly different individual as a new discovery. In the 19th century splitters predominated. Taxonomy was largely based on the idea of a 'type'. In museums all over the world there is a heavily guarded special room where the 'type specimens' are kept. These were the first individuals of a species or race to be described and accepted as sacrosanct by an International Committee. They were the standard to which all other specimens should be compared, irrespective of how normal or aberrant they might have been. On this basis

The common, reynard, cur or terrier fox.

Bulldog or mastiff type.

some biologists created large numbers of species or races, each with only a few distinguishing characters. A lot of these have been scrapped in modern times and the idea of race as a biological concept has fallen out of favour.

Foxes were not immune from this process. Most people (at least those who had any opinions on the subject) used to think that there were three main types of fox in Britain and even more local races. There was the *Common, Reynard, Cur* or *Terrier Fox*. This was the small, short-legged, red, Home Counties style fox that was chased about on horseback. Then there was the *Bulldog* or *Mastiff* type which was a short-legged, dark,

Greyhound type.

thickset fox with a broad head and a short snout. Although not exclusive to the area, this was mainly thought to live in the mountainous parts of Wales. Finally there was the *Greyhound* fox which resembled a small wolf. It had a large body, long rangy legs, a grey coat and a grizzly mask, and careered through the Scottish Highlands, devouring all lambs and grouse in its path. Together with other northern European foxes, this was at one time dignified with a third, subspecific Latin name, *crucigera*. The fact that at any one time and place you now found foxes in a variety of sizes and colours was thought to be due to these once distinct types having interbred to varying degrees. They were still to be found in their 'pure' form only in a few remote Kentish farmyards, Welsh valleys or Scottish glens.

Foxes do vary in size both within and between populations, but a lot of information is required before you can decide what these variations mean in terms of the British fox population as a whole. Firstly you have to de-

cide what you mean by size. In our own minds size is a one dimensional concept – things are either bigger or smaller. In the real world, however, the only solid object whose size expands or contracts in one dimension is a perfect sphere. Foxes are not spherical (unless they've been living inside a pork pie factory for a long time). When you have something which is fox-shaped things are not so simple. Is a long thin fox bigger or smaller than a short fat one? In the natural history journals size records for foxes are usually expressed in weight. There are a lot of articles entitled 'A very big fox from Such and Such a place', which describe, say, a 28½ lb fox from Worcestershire. Nobody writes articles entitled 'A very small fox from Somewhereshire'. This demonstrates two points. First, weight is not a very good measure of size because you may happen to have caught a very fat fox or one that has just eaten a big meal. Furthermore weight, like volume, increases approximately as the cube of linear dimensions so that it exaggerates the significance of bigger animals. Secondly, most foxes are somewhere in between the extremes of very big or very small and it is the average (or mean) of all the individuals in a sample from an area that gives a better measure of what foxes are like in that particular place.

The standard measurements that are made on mammals are the body weight, head and body length, tail length, the length of the hind foot and the height of the ear. The one dimensional size of each animal is somewhere inside these. There are mathematical techniques for extracting such things but they are not for the faint-hearted or for those who can't afford a medium-sized computer. If you measured 100 things on a fox then its size and shape could vary in 99 dimensions (we are talking here of mathematical dimensions which go on to infinity, wherever that is). Fortunately for our sanity they don't, and for practical purposes head and body length is usually a good approximation of overall size.

There are two main trends in the size of foxes in the UK. As you go further north they generally get larger, and as you go further west they get smaller. Neither of these is absolute and they can change with local circumstances. For instance foxes from most parts of Scotland are bigger than those from the south of England. However foxes living in the suburbs of south Glasgow are much smaller than those from surrounding hill areas in the Southern Uplands and around Loch Lomond to the north, and resemble foxes from London. Foxes from mountainous areas often seem larger than those from adjacent lowland but the difference is usually too small to be certain.

Another old adage of descriptive biology is Bergmann's Rule (named after a 19th-century German biologist called Carl Bergmann, who first described it). This states that animals get bigger as you go further north in their range. This is certainly the case with foxes, and having a range which extends from the Sahara to the Arctic they provide a good model for studying such variations. While there are theories as to why Bergmann's Rule should exist it is purely empirical and not really a 'rule'. Many species seem to conform to it, but others show no clear trends and some, such as the stoat, actually get bigger as you go to the south and smaller as you go north. The standard explanation for Bergmann's Rule is to do with temperature regulation and depends upon simple geometry. The larger a body becomes, the proportionally greater is its volume in relation to its surface area. Therefore in a colder climate it loses heat more slowly. Those who have criticised such an explanation point out that the fox has a perfectly good fur coat which it takes everywhere with it. Foxes from the north of

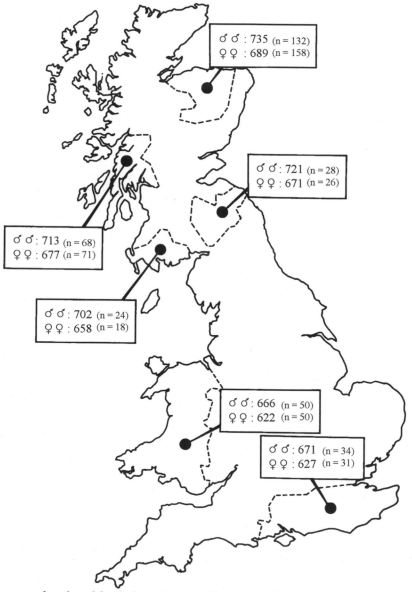

♂ ♂ : 735 (n = 132)
♀ ♀ : 689 (n = 158)

♂ ♂ : 721 (n = 28)
♀ ♀ : 671 (n = 26)

♂ ♂ : 713 (n = 68)
♀ ♀ : 677 (n = 71)

♂ ♂ : 702 (n = 24)
♀ ♀ : 658 (n = 18)

♂ ♂ : 666 (n = 50)
♀ ♀ : 622 (n = 50)

♂ ♂ : 671 (n = 34)
♀ ♀ : 627 (n = 31)

The average head and body lengths in millimetres of adult foxes from different parts of the British Isles; n=number of animals measured in each area (English and Welsh data from The Red Fox *by H.G. Lloyd).*

In summer, after moulting, the fox can look very sleek and thin.

Russia and Canada have extremely thick coats with very long hairs which in the past have been much in demand by furriers. Measurement of heat transmission through through such coats shows that they are good enough insulators in themselves to make body size irrelevant for temperature control.

However the volume of the body may still be important. In line with the above geometry, bigger foxes have a larger internal volume in which they can store proportionally more fat reserves than smaller foxes. Physiologists have studied the energy expenditure of different sized mammals and have come up with something which is usually called the 'Mouse – Elephant Curve'. This shows that per unit weight, large mammals use much less energy to keep themselves going than small mammals. Therefore a large fox is not only able to build up much greater fat reserves during times of the year when food is easily available, it also uses them more efficiently during tougher times when it can't find food so readily. In hard winter frosts or when snow is lying deep on the ground, it can travel further to find enough to eat to keep it going without dying of starvation in the process. This would mean that larger foxes are better adapted to living in more northerly climates and in mountainous areas. Fossil evidence shows that foxes also became larger during colder periods in the past such as the last glaciation in Europe. Big foxes still need more food than small ones in absolute terms so that in milder climates smaller foxes are probably better off. This leads to natural selection maintaining a size difference along temperature gradients, whether they be north-south, east-west or highland-lowland. The technical term for this kind of gradual change in an animal population over long distances is a 'cline'. These trends are real

	NORTH OF SCOTLAND		SOUTH OF ENGLAND	
Dog foxes	Average	Range	Average	Range
Head & Body	735	655-804	671	600-755
Tail	438	359-506	412	375-470
Hind Foot	174	155-189	152	135-170
Ear	99	91-112	93	85-100
Weight	7.19	4.51-9.50	6.67	5.50-8.20
Vixens				
Head & Body	689	576-750	627	570-700
Tail	405	348-696	385	335-420
Hind Foot	161	145-179	141	125-150
Ear	95	84-105	89	90-95
Weight	6.06	3.94-8.50	5.41	3.50-6.70

The body measurements in millimetres and weight in kilograms for adult foxes from the North and South of the British Isles.

but not very large and can only be demonstrated by measuring a lot of animals. On average foxes from the north of Scotland are 10 percent larger than those from the south of England. They have relatively longer legs, and shorter tails and ears. In both places dog foxes are 7 percent bigger than vixens. Why should this be? Dog foxes are more likely to disperse away from the place where they were born than vixens and when they do so they generally travel longer distances. When they settle down they have bigger home ranges than vixens on the same site and are more likely to go off on occasional explora-tory rambles around the surrounding countryside. Their slightly larger size than vixens is probably related to this greater mobility and the need to defend a territory, with the ex-tra demands on energy these requirements impose.

How do you know foxes are about?

Being largely nocturnal and wary, foxes are not all that easy to observe. Sometimes you will see one in the headlights of a car at night, or, if you're really keen, you can get up very early during the middle of the summer and watch foxes going about their normal activities in daylight. Even then it's helpful if you know that they're there to begin with and this will depend upon looking for their signs beforehand.

Smell You can occasionally get a whiff of fox when walking along a track or hedgerow. This is where one has urinated along the way in order to mark its ground, much as dogs do. The smell is very pungent and easy to recognise once you know what it is, but difficult to describe in words. If you ever get to handle a live fox it will probably pee on you. Fox droppings do not in themselves smell very strongly (to us) but they are sometimes urinated on as well. This is an easier way of finding out what fox urine smells like.

Scats Fox faecal droppings are given various names but 'scat' (from the Greek for dung) is the most usual one. These are found along the sides of

tracks and on prominent objects such as large clumps of grass or the carcasses of dead animals. They vary in appearance, depending upon what the fox has been eating. Usually they're formed of compressed hair with a few bones and teeth included. Rabbit hair gives a light grey colour whereas vole hair makes the scats much darker. Bird remains are generally grey in colour with a surface layer that dries out to white. During the summer beetle parts appear in scats and sometimes you can find ones which are entirely covered with shiny beetle wing cases. When the fox has been eating mainly fruit the scats are very dark and friable. At the other extreme when it has been scavenging a sheep or deer carcass you get long straggly white or brown droppings.

Fox scats are usually about 2 centimetres (0.8 inch) in diameter. When they're composed of hair they rarely come out in

Scat.

one lump, but break up into two or three sections, with the last one having a characteristic point. The length of this point depends upon the length of hairs composing it, with sheep's wool producing the longest. Scats composed mainly of insect or fruit remains tend to be smaller and less regular. There generally isn't any problem about confusing fox scats with the droppings of other carnivores. Dog faeces are usually much more bulky, have no definite form and smell disgusting. Domestic cat droppings are much

Fox scats in typically obvious position.

smaller and are usually buried. Should you be in a position to come across them, wildcat faeces are left in similar positions to those of foxes but are smaller and have a very regular bullet shape. Badger droppings tend to be dark and irregular and are left in characteristic pits that the animal has dug next to trails.

Hair When you see a track through the grass that passes next to a thorn bush, or especially when it goes through a barbed wire fence, you are quite likely to find hairs that have been caught from passing animals. If a fox has been through, you will often find the long guard hairs from its back. These are basically red, with some black and grey bands, depending upon the actual colour of the fox and whereabouts on the back they came from. Holes in the ground that have been visited by a fox may also have hairs caught on protruding bits of root.

Tracks Impressions of a fox's feet can be found when it has walked across soft ground, drying mud, and especially fresh snow. The marks are made by fleshy pads on the ends of the four toes together with a central hind pad. A fox's feet are quite small but size is not a very good basis for recognition as impressions always suggest that the animal making them is bigger than it is, particularly in snow where the edges start to melt and enlarge the print. A fox's track can be recognised by the shape and relationships of the main parts, although the clarity of these depends on the type of ground on which they were made. In general the foot mark is longer than it is wide and the pad marks of the toes are separate and not squashed together like those of a dog. On a very clear print you can sometimes see the marks of fur that is in the central space between the toes. The five pads are more or less the same size and there is a gap in the middle between them all. The

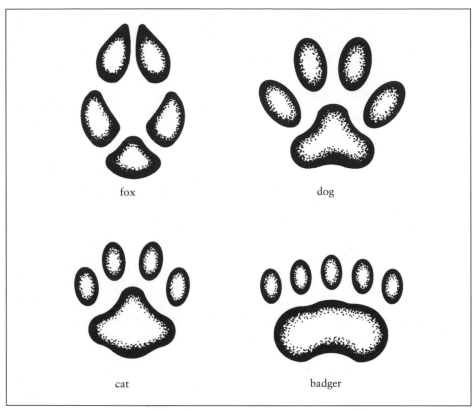

Comparison of fox, dog, cat and badger prints.

animal most likely to be confused with a fox is a small dog. Dog foot marks are much more circular and the hind pad is relatively bigger and fits in between the other four. Cat foot marks are circular and the four toes are arranged in an even circle around the front of the foot. Badgers leave a mark in which the hind pad is very large and five toe marks are arranged in an almost straight line in front of it. The successive footprints of a fox are virtually in a straight line and when it is walking the hind foot marks overprint the front ones, but this is only really apparent in snow where a lot of good prints can be seen. In the same circumstances a dog's front and hind footprints are set outside each other as dogs tend to walk with their bodies at a slight angle to the direction in which they're going.

Earths Fox dens vary in size from single-holed tubes to sets of interconnected tunnels with up to a dozen entrances. Well dug earths are found in light soils. They are likely to be on south-facing slopes and in cover, such as gorse or small copses. The entrance hole can be quite small, around 20 centimetres (8 inches), but well established earths are generally larger than this and have the floor of the entrance dug out into a fan of soil. This is most obvious on sandy ground where the fan of light soil may be visible from some distance away. Old fox earths are most likely to be confused with badger sets, but the latter usually have well defined paths leading up to them, the soil is pushed away into a heap some distance from the entrance and there may be piles of old bedding (grass and leaves) nearby, which foxes do not use. However foxes are opportunists and, while quite capable of digging, they often just enlarge old rabbit burrows or take over discarded ends of a large badger sett. They may even move into old drains. On hill ground many dens are made in cairns where the fox crawls into the shelter underneath suitable piles of rocks and boulders. There are often many potential den sites in an area which are partly excavated and may be used in rotation over several years or kept for an emergency if the cubs need to be moved. During the spring the fact that cubs are present is shown by a selection of decomposing prey remains which build up at the entrance. Otherwise the best way to find out if a fox is using a hole is to stick your head down it and sniff.

Typical remains from nesting bird eaten by fox: breast bone and wings from young black-headed gull.

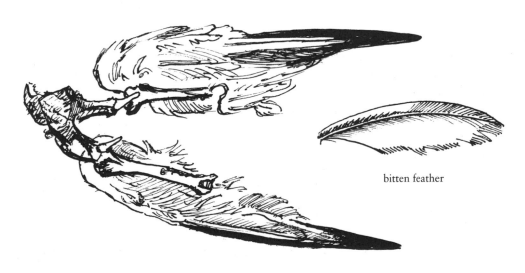

bitten feather

Vixen carrying a carcase of a young lapwing to her cubs.

Prey Small prey are eaten whole but there may be signs of digging into vole runways in the grass or into nests of young rabbits. Larger items are chewed by foxes and bits may be left behind or cached. If you find a pair of bird's wings cleanly bitten off and nothing else, this is likely to be a fox. Chunks of bird or rabbit may be found that have been cached by being partially buried under piles of leaves. In the spring in hill areas you can find whole lambs' heads cached under tufts of grass.

Calls Foxes can sometimes be heard calling during the night, particularly in the middle of winter. These sounds vary from bursts of three or four short, high-pitched barks to single intense shrieks or hysterical sounding screams, some of which can quite unnerving if heard at close quarters (however, they are used to advertise a fox's presence and are not produced by animals in distress). While the barks might be easily overlooked or thought to be coming from a small dog, the more violent calls are difficult to miss; some less intense howls might be mistaken for the hoots of owls.

Nature red in tooth ...

We concluded in an earlier chapter that while foxes are classified as carnivores they are not in the sabre tooth tiger class. So what do they actually eat? There are several ways of finding out.

If you have access to a lot of dead foxes, the best way is to look at the contents of their stomachs. This is not a very pleasant job but since the remains are at worst only semi-digested it gives you the best impression of the relative quantities of different things in the diet. You may still have to do some detective work to be able to recognise what's there. Small prey, particularly rodents, are generally swallowed whole. Larger items like rabbits and birds are chewed up and only present in part, so that you have to look for the important bits. Usually there are teeth, hairs or feathers which are identifiable, either whole or under a microscope. When foxes have been feeding on carrion like sheep and deer there may just be a large, unpleasant wodge of meat and fat, often with very few hairs attached. Apart from these kinds of major items there will be bits of small things like beetles or worms.

Much more material can be obtained by collecting fox faeces (scats) and looking at their composition. Fox droppings are not usually unpleasant to handle, although it is advisable to 'glove' them in a polythene bag and then dry them out and sterilise them before you touch them with your bare hands. Even then there may be a risk of picking up eggs from gut parasites. Some roundworms produce eggs with a fibrous shell which is resistant to extreme desiccation and even laboratory preservatives like formalin. Fox scats are commonly found along tracks through farmland, forestry and across hill land and can be collected quite easily, particularly during the winter. In summer they decompose much

A successful vole-hunter.

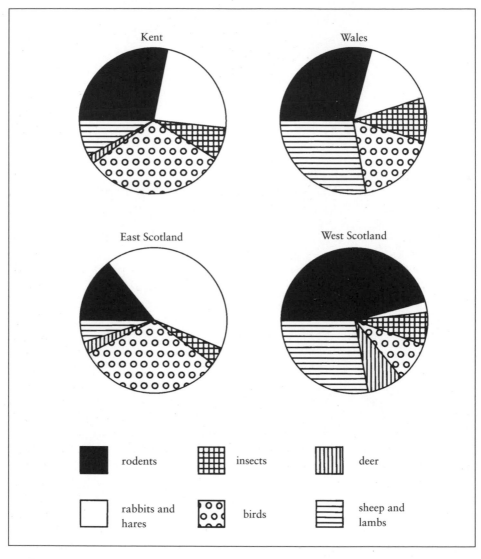

Kent

Wales

East Scotland

West Scotland

	rodents		insects		deer
	rabbits and hares		birds		sheep and lambs

The relative proportions of the main items in a fox's diet in different parts of the British Isles (English and Welsh data taken from The Red Fox *by H.G. Lloyd).*

Predator and prey (short-tailed vole).

more quickly and may be hidden by vegetation. This can lead to some bias if you
want to find out what foxes are eating
throughout the year. The other problem with
scats is that they represent the end product
of digestion so that only the more resistant parts
of the diet come through. Voles, for instance, are
eaten whole, so that a scat from a fox that has eaten
t h e m comes out a bit like an owl pellet with a compressed mass of
dark hair, inside which there are bits of teeth and skeleton. Not all the
skeleton survives as some is dissolved in the acids of the stomach, but the
digestible portion of the meal is quite low. Similarly if a fox eats a beetle
the hard parts of the exoskeleton, particularly the wing covers (elytra)
appear unchanged. At the other extreme, if a fox eats a worm, most of the
body is digested and only the very small, hard spines (chaetae) that the
worm has all down its sides will survive. Even worse, if a fox eats the
intestines or body organs of a dead sheep or deer then nothing will appear
after digestion. Therefore analysing a fox diet from scats requires some
caution.

Another source of information is to look at the remains that are left
lying about outside breeding dens. Fox dens are pretty messy places and
bits and pieces of fur and fowl are generally found rotting in the vicinity.
Smaller morsels are regurgitated by the parents and eaten by the cubs, but
more often the adults choose to carry back bigger items such as rabbits,

lambs, pheasants or grouse, depending on the habitat. The cubs can only eat part of these, and chew and play around with the rest. Seeing an accumulation of bits and pieces of this kind doesn't make a very good impression on the owner of the ground where the den is, but it may not be representative of the whole diet.

Much is made of the catholicity of foxes' tastes and how they are prepared to eat anything from grapes to bread wrappers. In one sense this is true. If you itemise all the different things that you can find in foxes' stomachs or scats from any one area, you generally get a very long list. However if you concentrate on the relative proportions of each, then in most country districts only a few make up the bulk of the diet. Some kinds of prey are commoner in particular habitats and foxes also have their own preferences. Part of this preference arises from the tendency of predators to expend more effort in eating things that are common. Animal behaviourists call this a 'search image'. Once a predator learns that a particular prey is plentiful it tends to concentrate on looking for that to the exclusion of rarer things. On top of that foxes do seem to have some actual taste preferences. Given the choice, they are more likely to eat short-tailed voles rather than other rodents. Conversely they avoid shrews, probably because these have glands on their sides which produce an unpleasant taste, and some of them also have a poisonous saliva.

The two most important single species that foxes prey on are rabbits

and short-tailed voles. In some places or years either or both of these can make up 75 percent of what is eaten. However their contribution to the diet varies in different parts of the British Isles. Rodents are taken everywhere, although more so in the west, and particularly where there is a lot of forestry. Short-tailed voles are always the commonest species that is eaten. In England and Wales brown rats come next in the league table of goodies, and after that long-tailed fieldmice and bank voles. All three of these are also eaten in Scotland but to a lesser extent than south of the border. Foxes eat rabbits and hares wherever they occur. In studies of diet these are generally listed together as 'Lagomorphs' because it is not always easy to tell the difference between the various species when you are faced with only some lumps of flesh and a few hairs. However the intake of rabbits far exceeds that of brown hares over most of the country, and particularly in the east. The main exception to this pattern is on Scottish grouse moors where mountain hares make up a significant part of the diet. The remains of insectivores such as shrews, moles and hedgehogs are only rarely observed in stomachs and scats, compared with their abundance in the countryside. As suggested above, they are probably defended by their unpleasant taste and smell, or, in the case of hedgehogs, by their spines.

Birds of various kinds are an important prey in the south and east of Britain. When body parts or feathers are found in fox stomachs, the species involved can usually be identified fairly easily by comparison with a reference collection. However when you're dealing with scats, the parts, including feathers, are generally too macerated and digested for this. The microscopic structure of feather barbs and barbules (the velcro-like structures that hold the feathers' vane together) can be examined to see which family the bird came from but it is rarely possible to be more specific than this. While a great variety of species are eaten by the fox, the bird family which receives most attention is the Galliformes – poultry and game birds. Chickens can form up to half the Galliformes taken, the rest being composed of whichever gamebirds are commonest in the area. In the south of England these are pheasants and partridges, in the east of Scotland mainly pheasants, and in central Scotland, red grouse. After Galliformes, the next commonest birds taken are songbirds, particularly the blackbird, but in the stomachs of foxes from Scotland I have found wrens, bullfinches and wheatears. The rest of the bird remains are made up in more or less equal proportions of pigeons, various ducks (mallards and ground-nesting species like teal), waders (lapwings and various plovers) and rails (mainly coots and moorhens). Along coasts foxes also regularly eat gulls, particularly during the breeding season. In fact any ground-nesting bird is likely to be eaten by foxes at some time or another. They will take any birds they can catch and the different types appear in the diet in proportion to their availability. You can also find the remains of egg shells in stomachs and scats, but they are usually too crunched to be identifiable with certainty.

Deer remains are rare in the south and east of Britain but are more frequent in the west of Scotland. Foxes do not prey on deer (except occasionally on fawns) but exploit them as carrion. Some of this is supplied by animals that have died in snow drifts, hit fences or been knocked down by vehicles. The rest comes from 'grallochs'. After a deer has been shot by a stalker the first thing he needs to do is remove the guts to stop them tainting the meat and to make carrying the carcass easier. This is done by slicing the belly with a sharp knife and pulling out the guts and lights with the hands. These, the grallochs, are left lying for the first scavenger that finds them.

Insects do not provide a major source of nutrition for foxes, but they are eaten regularly during the summer. Occasionally you will come across a scat which is studded with shiny beetle wing cases. Most beetles are presumably eaten from choice, but you also sometimes find maggots and carrion beetles in fox stomachs. These are regarded as a sign that whatever else the fox was eating was already dead and in a moderately advanced state of decay. Urban foxes and some of those living in parts of the Home Counties are known to eat earthworms in substantial numbers, but they are a much rarer occurrence in the stomachs of true country foxes. Similarly vegetables and fruits are eaten, apparently more so in the south of England than elsewhere. Here foxes may sometimes fill themselves with blackberries or windfall apples. Frogs and fish are also taken. There is no evidence that foxes go fishing but they will scavenge dead fish if the chance arises. I once looked inside the stomachs of several foxes from the west of Scotland which had been caught near to where a fish lorry had crashed, and which had been stuffing themselves with herrings. All sorts of odd organic and inorganic materials may be found in fox stomachs, but such esoteric eating habits are more typical of urban foxes rather than country ones. Urban fox biologists are liable to bore people with stories of the number of used condoms that they've found in stomachs. The equivalent for students of the country fox are the small rubber rings that are used to castrate young rams (if you don't know how these are used, come and see me afterwards).

Do foxes kill lambs?

Next to hunting this seems to be one of the main bones of contention in country fox biology. On the one hand apologists say that foxes are blameless for any sheep or lamb deaths, and that they either don't kill any healthy lambs, or that the number is so trivial that any control of foxes on this count is unjustifiable. At the other extreme there are sheep farmers who claim that foxes are a threat to their livelihood and that all efforts should be made to exterminate them in the vicinity of their farms. Who is right?

The problem only really arises in hill farming areas such as central Wales, the north of England and the west and north of Scotland. There are plenty of sheep elsewhere but they don't feature very much in the fox's diet. In hill areas sheep and lamb remains can sometimes make up half of the contents of foxes' stomachs in the spring and early summer. Even the most anti-fox people have rarely suggested that foxes kill adult sheep so that the bits of wool and mutton that are in foxes' stomachs and scats during the winter are concluded to be the result of scavenging on dead carcasses. From March to July lamb remains appear in stomachs. These are easily identifiable. The wool of young lambs has a tight curly appearance and a flat cross section which is quite distinct from the wool of adult sheep. Foxes are fond of chewing bits off some of the things that they eat and when they are eating lambs you frequently find ears and sets of small hooves in the stomach. They particularly like biting off noses, presumably because they are soft and juicy, and these are also common. In samples of foxes killed in different parts of the west of Scotland during the lambing season, lambs made up between 35 and 45 percent of the stomach contents. However it is not possible to put the bits and pieces together and discover the condition of these lambs when they were eaten. They could have been predated or they could have died naturally and been scavenged.

Before condemning the fox on the basis of this sort of information it is necessary to look at the background of sheep farming in Britain. At one time wool production was a major part of the British economy. In Tudor times sheep were concentrated in England. With the coming of agricultural improvements, land enclosure and better communications, sheep farming was increasingly moved to the peripheral parts of the UK where the production of other crops was more difficult. The extreme instance of this was the Highland Clearances which took place during the first half of the 19th century. Large areas of ground in the north and west of Scotland

Northumberland hill farm.

were cleared of crofters and their cattle and potatoes, and repopulated with sheep by the landowners. The hill farms now there are direct descendants of the ones that were set up then. However, there is no longer a big market for wool, and left to themselves these farms are not profitable. They are largely dependent upon Government subsidies for survival. The farmers get so much money per ewe. These subsidies are paid for social reasons as without them the areas would become depopulated. Despite this in the past thirty years many hill farms have been sold into forestry. The soil is acid, wet and not very productive. Many ewes are wintered on the hill and some are lambed there, often without supplementary feed. Obviously the husbandry varies from farm to farm depending upon the type of ground available, but ewes are often in poor condition at the end of the winter and a number of them usually die during lambing. Some lambs are stillborn and others die of malnutrition or starvation early in life. The land is exposed and unseasonal weather such as late snow can be very damaging to production. There is a term in hill farming called 'black loss' which is the difference between the number of lambs you expect to get in the spring and the number that actually appear when the ewes and lambs are rounded up for marking in the summer. The proportion of ewes with lambs in parts of Scotland can be as low as 60 percent.

How much contribution do foxes make to this loss? It is not an easy subject to study because most of the evidence disappears down foxes' gullets. However, dead lambs are occasionally recovered with injuries showing that they were healthy when killed by a fox. All it takes is one genuine dead lamb to be found and most farmers will assume that the fox is guilty until proved innocent. Some will tell you that it takes thirty or more lambs to rear a den of fox cubs, but nobody who has examined the subject has concluded that foxes kill more than 1 or 2 percent of the overall annual

Cheviot ewe with young lamb stamps defiance at fox: her fear is also for her first-born lamb, which is hidden but vulnerable.

Foxes will not turn their noses up at carrion.

lamb crop in hill areas, although locally predation may be greater. On smallholdings with 500 ewes or less farmers responding to surveys have claimed a loss of around 4 percent. Given the marginal economics of hill sheep farming, this may be important to many people. Farmers also say that this is the loss in the face of extensive fox control and that if foxes were left to their own devices it would be greater. Trials with captive foxes suggest that they don't much like the taste of lamb. However these may not be very realistic. If I was given the choice of Irish stew or lobster thermidore I'd probably choose the lobster. On the other hand if I'd been stomping up and down a fell for a fortnight and there wasn't anything else to eat, I'd probably settle for fried vole (I'd draw the line at raw ones).

While there is a lot of carrion about in hill areas there are also a lot of scavengers competing for it. The populations of species like ravens, kites and even eagles can be affected by how many dead sheep there are. Crows, buzzards, gulls and sheepdogs also help clean up what is available every spring, and what they don't get ends up inside maggots. In some places there may not be much else for foxes to eat but lambs. However, given the large home range sizes of hill foxes and the high density of sheep, even the most ovicidal fox would be hard put to it to make a serious impact on a lambing flock. To some degree the fox is made a scapegoat for the problems of hill farming in inhospitable areas. Notwithstanding, sheep farmers will continue to demand that fox control is carried out, preferably paid for by somebody else.

Serial killers

Even the most mild mannered carnivores have to eat, so evolution has programmed them with the basic abilities to hunt and kill other animals. Learning plays a part in determining what an individual fox chooses to look for and eat in a particular place and probably has a role in fine tuning hunting behaviour, but most of the mechanics for capturing and disposing of prey are inherited. Usually hunting, killing and eating follow a natural progression. However hunting is always going to be a chancy business and there are likely to be circumstances where a fox that has eaten still comes across prey. It would be advantageous to kill this and store it away for future use as there are always going to be times when hunting is less successful. Foxes do this by cacheing unwanted prey, burying it under leaves, grass or loose soil. Observations in gull colonies have shown that foxes will cache eggs in sand and come back and eat them two months later, and in experiments they remembered where hens' eggs were buried for up to three months. In most places in Britain fresh meat is not going to last that long. Foxes are quite prepared to chew decomposing sheep and deer carcasses and eat maggots, so they may be able to use these caches for as long as they remain intact. During snowy spells and in more northerly areas the food can remain available for a long time. Where they have a lot of separate cached food sites, foxes may use urine marks at these as a kind of

book-keeping system to remind themselves whether it's worth digging them up again.

When a rabbit suddenly appears in front of your nose and makes a dash for safety you aren't going to be a very succesful predator if you have to sit down and work out a plan of campaign for catching it. Under these circumstances, carnivores rely on spontaneous reflexes for catching and killing which seem to be completely separate from the motivations for hunting and eating. Should panicking animals suddenly present themselves in numbers this reflex is repeatedly triggered and leads to the kind of surplus killing that is shown by foxes (and other carnivores) in a hen house or a gull colony. In the past, when many people had open poultry runs, this kind of purposeless slaughter was one of the things that fixed the image of the fox as a serious nuisance in the minds of country folk. Such chasing and catching just for the hell of it is not necessarily confined to foxes and chickens. It can be seen in the behaviour of a dog running after a ball, and perhaps in a child running after a pigeon and a landowner riding after a pack of hounds which are in turn chasing (to bring the argument full circle) a fox.

The quick brown fox ...

The archetypal sentence in the English language that contains all the letters of the alphabet is:

   The Quick Brown Fox Jumps Over The Lazy Dog

Of course there are other, less well known ones:

   Light Pink Jaws Amazed Very Quiet Fox Cubs

   Vole Gazes On As Damp Fox Jabs Quarry With Stick

   Judge How Zebras Marvel At Quickstep And Foxtrot

   Poor Badgers Just Quake To Flout A Vixen's Crazy Whims

   Bluff Reynard Hoaxed Pack With Zany Jinks Over Quagmire

   Squawk By Dazed Cock Pheasant As Vixen Aims For Jugular

   Chummy Dog Foxes Wave Tails At Joke In Probing Quiz

   etc.

How many?

In order to answer a lot of the questions that people ask in fox biology, you need to have some idea of how many foxes there are – are populations going up or down, does hunting or control have any effect on fox numbers, how many rabbits are eaten by foxes, is rabies likely to take hold in a place? etc. Theoretically the idea of population density is quite simple. It's just the number of animals in a particular area (for foxes the most sensible unit is a square kilometre). However for a secretive animal like the fox, the practical difficulties of counting numbers accurately are severe.

There are two ways of addressing such a problem. One is to actually put in the effort and count all the foxes present. You could try and trap all the animals on an area and remove them or mark and release them, but you can never quite be sure that you've accounted for them all like this. The most accurate way is to catch the animals in an area and mark them with collars that transmit radio signals and then release them and follow their movements. Over a period of trapping, observation and radio-tracking you can eventually be sure that you have accounted for most of the individuals present. This is an extremely labour intensive and expensive business and can only be done in a limited area. Not only that but catching foxes isn't all that easy! A more extensive method is to count all the active breeding dens in an area. This is less accurate because even if you ensure that you find all the dens there may be a number of foxes that do not breed for various reasons and you will tend to underestimate the density in some places.

The alternative approach is to use something that is an 'index' of the population. This is a measurement that goes up and down with the number of animals present without actually telling you how many are there. It allows you to say that foxes are more numerous in one place or year as compared with another, and you can then compare this with other things that may have changed. Commonly used indices are the number of foxes caught each year by hunts or fox control societies, or the number of scats collected along regularly walked tracks. The main problem is that for these kinds of measurements to be meaningful, the same effort has to be put into collecting the information in each place or year. Using the number of foxes killed by organisations that are ostensibly in the business of fox control to find out what is happening to the population might seem like a suspiciously circular process. It probably would be if control was actually having an effect on depressing the national fox population. However nowadays fox control is much more localised than it has been in the past, so that even if the population is cleared out of a place, more foxes will move in and the numbers caught each year give an indication of how many there are in the surrounding countryside.

Fox population densities vary enormously between different habitats and in different parts of Britain. The highest numbers of rural foxes are found in the south and south-west of the country with approximately one den per square kilometre and between 2 and 4 adult foxes in the same area. Naturally this number of foxes will increase after breeding by whatever the average litter size is in the area. During the summer there could be around 10 foxes per square kilometre (0.4 sq. mile), but this decreases through the year as a result of mortality and dispersal. By contrast, in the Scottish Highlands it is easier to talk about how many square kilometres there are per fox. Surveys on sporting estates suggest that there is on average about one den to every 25 square kilometres (9 sq. miles). The population density is in the order of one fox to every 10 square kilometres (3 sq. miles), at least twenty times lower than in the south of England.

Statistics on the number of foxes killed every year by sporting estates, fox destruction clubs and organisations like the Forestry Commission all suggest that the British fox population has been increasing since 1945. The single biggest cause of this increase is that there are fewer gamekeepers now than there were before 1939. One of the most noticeable things to stand out from this steady increase was an upward blip in the number of foxes killed just after myxomatosis devastated the rabbit population around 1953/4. Myxomatosis is a South American rabbit disease that was imported into Britain from France in 1952. Although nobody's sure exactly

how it got into the country, once it was here farmers spread it everywhere within two years by moving infected rabbits about. It is estimated that 99 percent of the rabbit population died because it had no resistance to such a new disease. Having got rid of the rabbits, farmers suddenly started panicking and wondering what the foxes were going to eat in case it turned out to be their livestock. A number of studies were made of the diet of foxes and it was concluded that they had largely switched to eating more small rodents in the absence of rabbits. This is not very suprising as, with no rabbits around, many places that had previously resembled billiard tables were now able to grow grass, and voles in particular were capable of taking advantage of the improved habitat. The increase in the number of foxes killed around 1954 could therefore have been due to a number of reasons. More control effort might have been made to counteract the imagined threat from foxes, the short term availablity of sick and moribund rabbits might have provided a superabundant food supply or the number of voles might suddenly have shot up. In recent years rabbits have developed immunity to myxomatosis and their numbers have largely recovered in the eastern parts of Britain.

One of the other main causes of increase in the number of foxes in places like Wales and the west and south of Scotland was the large scale afforestation that took place in the 1960s and 70s. Huge areas of what had been open sheep walks were fenced off, ploughed and planted with conifers. Since it takes the trees ten to fifteen years to grow to sufficient size to block out the sunlight there is a long period of unrestrained grass growth and this encourages short-tailed vole populations. Once they become established these voles go through characteristic changes in numbers which are usually called 'cycles'. This word gives an exaggerated impression of their regularity. Vole densities reach a peak almost simultaneously over large areas, crash the next year, stay low for another one or two years and then peak again. This gives a regular population change that averages out within a period of about four years. Despite intensive research for a long time nobody still really understands the processes that cause these cycles, but they have a significant effect on the numbers and breeding of the predators that eat voles, foxes among them. The predator numbers show a parallel but slightly delayed response to the fluctuations of their prey. These kinds of population cycles in predators and prey occur commonly in northern latitudes. Much work was done in the early years of animal ecology using the fur returns from the Hudson's Bay Company which recorded the number of pelts processed from northern Canada for nearly a hundred years. Here the main prey species is the varying hare

Cycles of vole numbers ...

which has a cycle period of around ten years. Foxes there show similar changes in numbers. One early theory was that these population cycles were related to the changes in the number of sun spots. At the time most ecologists reacted to this suggestion by asking when the flying saucers were going to arrive and detailed measurements did not support the idea. However nowadays many people accept that there are cyclical changes in the output of solar energy that can have effects on the earth's weather and the productivity of vegetation. These may be translated into variations in the breeding and density of herbivorous animals, which in turn can affect the numbers of their predators or at least give rise to the synchronisation of changes over large areas. The exact processes are probably complex and are modified by the characteristics of each species. Larger, more long lived animals like hares and grouse fluctuate with a ten-or eleven-year cycle, whereas short-lived animals like voles and lemmings are operating on a sub-multiple of this and peak at three- to five-year intervals. Predators like foxes could have a feedback role in this situation by helping to drive prey populations down after they have peaked.

... and a crash

One pad in the grave

Foxes in captivity seem to have a life span similar to that of dogs. If looked after they can live for fifteen to twenty years. However very few wild foxes even remotely approach this. If you want to understand the dynamics of a fox population it is important to know the ages of the animals that compose it. How can you tell the age of foxes?

With live foxes this is not very easy. You could catch them as cubs and mark them with something like an ear tag and then recapture them later, but, while very accurate, this could only be used in very limited circumstances. Once they get beyond six months old, young foxes are almost indistinguishable in size and weight from adults. The long bones in the legs do not stop growing until about nine months and before this it may be possible to feel a notch near the joints in the hind leg where the top of the bone is still separate from the shaft. The teeth wear down through life but the degree depends upon what the foxes have been eating and where they live. Those in the Home Counties and the suburbs of cities can keep a full set of teeth until old age, assuming they survive that long. Foxes from the west of Scotland spend their lives poking about in acid grassland for voles and chewing decomposing sheep carcasses. The minute number of individuals that survive to six or seven years old end up with a nice set of abscesses.

Finding out the age of dead foxes is more reliable. During their first year the gaps (sutures) between the bones in the base of the skull are still open. After that the best way of telling the age is to look for annual growth rings in the teeth. The lower jaw needs to be removed and softened in acid to dispose of the hard calcium in the teeth and bones. These are then cut into very thin sections and stained with a suitable dye for examination under a microscope. The main body of a tooth consists of a hard bone called dentine which is covered in an even harder layer of enamel. Where the tooth fits into its socket in the jaw there is plug of less dense bone called cementum surrounding the root. This continues to grow throughout life but at a different rate during each season. When growth is fast in the summer and autumn a wide light staining layer is produced. During the late spring growth slows down and a dark staining band appears. It is not certain why these bands are formed but the slowing in growth may be related to hormonal changes during the annual moult.

The greatest age that rural foxes are known to live to is ten years. How-

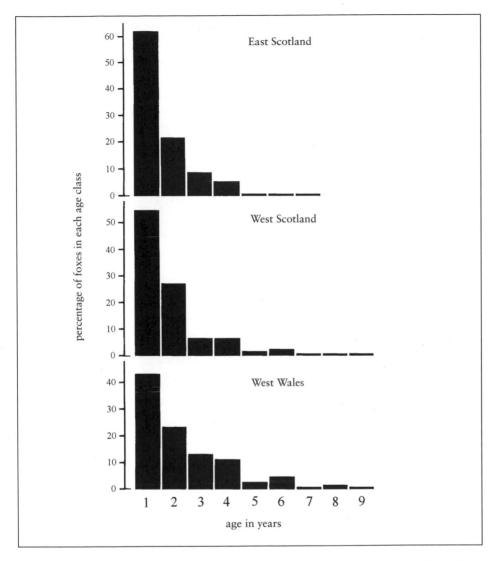

The age structure of three fox populations (Welsh data from The Red Fox *by H.G.Lloyd)*

ever for every hundred foxes born only one is likely to survive this long and this is only in some populations. Where there is a lot of control, as in eastern Scotland, most foxes are one year old and 98 percent have died by the age of five. The average annual mortality rate is about 60 percent. The death rate of younger animals is greater than this. Around 90 percent of foxes that are snared during the late summer and autumn are in their first year. It is not easy to find a place where there is no human control to compare with this but the situation that probably comes closest to it is a fox population studied by Gwyn Lloyd in the west of Wales. Here 90 percent of foxes have died by the age of five, and the average annual mortality rate is 35 percent. Even if people didn't kill foxes very few of them would live to a ripe old age, although one can only speculate on what they would actually die from. In North America foxes are predated on by bigger carnivores like wolves and coyotes but there are no longer such threats in Britain. Very few foxes seem to be in a sufficiently poor condition to be dying of starvation although some can be found throughout the year that have no body fat reserves. If foxes were left to their own devices the most likely cause of death would be diseases of various kinds. Sixty percent mortality might seem like a heavy annual toll but this is occurring in a part of the country where fox populations have been increasing over the past fifty years. Mathematical models of fox populations suggest that annual mortality has to be greater than 75 percent before numbers go into a decline.

Home on the range

For a long time people treated the fox as if, outside the breeding season, it had no social behaviour. Foxes were animals that occasionally appeared out of the night in ones or twos and then disappeared again. When biologists first started to study the social life of carnivores they were attracted to diurnal, group-living types like wolves, wild dogs and lions. There was more money and kudos in going off to romantic, far away study areas and watching these animals co-operate to photogenically disembowel assorted deer and antelopes. Skulking around the countryside looking for fox droppings didn't have the same appeal.

This scenario was changed by the development of the technique of radio-tracking. This is sometimes called radio-telemetry, but telemetry means the sending of information via a radio signal, whereas tracking relies mainly on radio-location using directional aerials. The basics of this had been around for a long time, but its use for animals depended on the appearance of miniature radio components that could be assembled into a very small transmitter, sometimes weighing only a few grams, and, equally important, very small, efficient batteries. These are fitted into a collar or harness that an animal like a fox can carry around for a year or more.

There are several ways of getting information from such a radio signal. The most straightforward method is to set up two or three large aerials on strategic high points and take bearings on the signal in order to find out where the fox is throughout the night. This sounds simple and is a reliable way of locating ships and aircraft. However these small transmitters are working on fairly long wavelengths, typically two to three metres. The transmitter also needs an aerial and it's impossible to attach a sufficiently large one to even a relatively big animal like a fox without interfering with the animal's behaviour. The collars are therefore not optimally tuned. The situation is more complicated by the fact that, being close to the ground, the vhf signal is affected by objects around it, just like a local radio broadcast. Listening

Fox wearing radio collar.

Foxes take avoiding action.

to the signal from a collar on a moving fox is a bit like listening to your car radio when you're near the edge of the local transmitter's range. Taking bearings on such a signal gives messy information and some of the directions you get can be completely out to lunch, having been reflected off nearby hills, fence lines or wet trees.

The other approach is to use the signal to home in on the animal that you're following. You are then more sure that you know exactly where it is and you can also sometimes see it. In recent years this has been helped by the use of night viewing equipment. These are binoculars or telescopes that have a section in them which electronically amplifies light. This introduces you to a spotty green world in which you can see behaviour that was previously hidden by the dark. Even night viewers need some light and observation is improved by other attachments. One is to fix a small capsule called a β-light to the collar. This is made of hollow glass with phosphor coated on the inside (like a TV screen) and contains a small quantity of radioactive gas which makes the phosphor glow in the dark. You can see these with the naked eye but they are a lot stronger through the night viewer and help you find a collared animal. Another aid is to attach a spot-light to the viewer that emits very dark red visible or short wavelength infra-red light. This is largely invisible to the mammalian eye but not to the electronics of the viewer. Carrying all this equipment around in the dark is a good recipe for a broken neck. In fact it may be impractical to follow most animals continuously. After a few weeks of tracking an individual you get a good idea of where it's likely to be and you can get there first, find a good position and waylay it. The information that you get this way may be a bit selective but it's better than nothing.

Given the imprecision of early radio-tracking it took a while to work out what foxes were doing throughout the night. The first debate centred around whether they were territorial or not. Animals generally live in a particular place. It is of obvious benefit to know where most of the things in your life are – where to eat, where to sleep, where to run to in the event of danger. This leads to the concept of a 'home range', somewhere that the animal is most familiar with and where it is most likely to be found. However it is at least a nuisance if you go out for a meal and discover that somebody else is already there and has eaten what you wanted for dinner, or you come home at night and find one of your neighbours sleeping in your bed. One simple way of sorting out this kind of situation (depending upon the intruder's sex) is to beat them up, kick them out and, having convinced them of your intentions, put up a lot of 'PRIVATE' and 'KEEP OUT' signs. You then have a territory.

Fighting foxes.

When it comes to scientific biology you have to demonstrate that this kind of thing is actually going on out in the field. The strict definition of a territory is 'a defended area'. The earliest suggestion that foxes were territorial came from the use of very high quality radio-location equipment in the USA. This showed that foxes in a high density population had ranges which hardly overlapped. This is *prima facie* evidence that defence is going on but it remained for people to actually see neighbouring residents repeatedly fighting at fixed points in order to prove that there were territorial boundaries: they have done so, with great difficulty, but established territory owners adapt to each other's presence and don't need to fight very much. They reinforce their possession by using chemical signals in urine and faeces which are recognised by intruders who realise, more often than not, that it is not worth getting involved in a fight. They then either retreat or, if they are transients looking for a territory of their own, keep moving on. Most studies of radio-collared foxes therefore measure home range size, which is the area which the animals habitually use but do not necessarily defend. This is usually bigger than territory size either because most animals trespass on their neighbour's ground to some extent when there is no immediate opposition or because most of the time foxes are not aware of such precise boundaries as we like to think of when drawing lines on a map. A more direct way of measuring territory size would be to analyse the signals that the foxes use by chemical analysis of the urine and faeces that are put down as markers. This requires very sophisticated equipment and our knowledge of communication via smell in mammals is still at an early stage. Another way is to inject a resident animal with a radioactive material that is excreted in the urine and then go around with a geiger counter looking for where the fox has marked. This has a limited use and is regarded with suspicion by the more environmentally conscious. Physical markers, such as bits of coloured plastic, could be put into bait and looked for in scats, as has been done for badgers, but this is much more difficult to use for foxes, as they have less regular habits and it is difficult to target sets of individuals as can be done with badgers.

Over the years a general picture of fox social behaviour has therefore emerged. The basic breeding group is a dog and a vixen. The dog fox has a slightly larger range than the vixen and may occasionally go off on exploratory forays through the surrounding countryside for one or two nights and then come back. The core parts of the pair's overlapping ranges are defended against intrusion from other foxes. When food is abundant some

of the vixens born in a territory will not leave during the winter and group ranges are established. These vixens hunt separately within the range and even sleep in different places, but during the breeding season generally only the oldest one produces cubs and the others help to feed them. Young dog foxes leave the territory of their birth and look for somewhere else to live. Some may keep moving continuously during the winter. Others take up temporary residence, living in the chinks in and between territories. While a territory looks like a uniform defended area if you draw a map of it using just the boundaries, in fact the resident foxes use parts of it selectively and there are usually patches of dead ground that subordinates can squeeze into. These young animals are most susceptible to control or food shortages and suffer a much higher mortality rate than the general population.

Fox range sizes vary a great deal in different habitats. The smallest recorded in mixed farming country in the USA are around half a square kilometre (123 acres). In Britain the nearest you get to this is in the southwest where ranges can average 0.75 square kilometre (185 acres), but in most rural areas in the south of England the typical range size is between 1.0 and 2.0 square kilometres (200-400 acres). At the other extreme in upland sheep farming areas ranges of 4.0 to 10.0 square kilometres (900-2,000 acres) are more typical, and 20 square kilometres (4,000 acres) has been recorded in the north of Scotland. For most fox populations there are general relationships between density and movement. The higher the population density the smaller the ranges and the less distance young animals disperse from where they were born, and vice versa.

Litter louts

Finding out the size of fox families is not as straightforward as it might at first seem. Obviously you could sit ouside dens and count the number of cubs that you see. This might seem alright at first but it has a number of drawbacks. Firstly it is very time consuming and you are unlikely ever to get a large sample to work on. Secondly you don't know that all the cubs that were originally born have survived to the stage when you are seeing them. Thirdly you can never guarantee that they are all out at the same time unless you are able to recognise individuals by their markings, or you have previously caught and tagged them.

In order to make meaningful, quantitative comparisons of the number of cubs conceived and born to vixens at different times and places, biologists need to find fixed points in the breeding season which they can study. Because of the problems outlined above, this is very difficult to do on living animals. As a result, the most detailed studies of fox breeding have been done by removing and examining the reproductive systems of dead animals. Back in the 'bad old days' dead foxes were relatively easy to collect. Gamekeepers and shepherds did, and still do, kill foxes on a routine basis, particularly during the breeding season. This is the time of year when foxes are considered to be the most serious threat to lambs and nesting game birds, and when control has the biggest impact on the fox population by reducing the next generation.

To get a complete description of reproduction you need to start at the stage of the egg and work forwards. If they breed at all, foxes only have one litter a year, so there are no complications about successive or overlapping families which you get in some mammals like rabbits and hares. Vixens are on heat, or receptive to mating, for up to a week. This is a stage in the annual reproductive cycle known as 'oestrus', during which eggs are shed from the ovary. The potential litter size in each vixen is determined by the number of eggs that grow in the two ovaries. When the eggs are released they are carried into ducts called the 'fallopian tubes', one of which leads to the top of each side of the paired uterus. This is when fertilisation takes place, after which the fertilised eggs start to develop and become embedded in the wall of the uterus where they become embryos. It is difficult to count eggs as such because they are microscopic and hard to find, and very few vixens are caught during the short period when eggs are observable. However the ovary and uterus go through characteristic changes which allow you to back track from later stages. These changes are related to the release of sequences of different reproductive hormones which control pregnancy.

Eggs develop in the ovary in small fluid filled cavities called Graafian follicles (after the person who first described them, a Dutch physiologist called Regnier de Graaf [1641-1673] – although since mammalian eggs hadn't been discovered yet, he didn't know what the follicles did). When each egg is ripe it bursts through the surface of the follicle into the body cavity and heads for a fallopian tube. The space that is left behind fills with spongy tissue and grows larger. Each develops into a body called a 'corpus luteum' (plural 'corpora lutea', meaning yellow bodies in Latin – at one time Latin was the universal language of science). You can see these bodies on the surface of the ovary throughout the summer after breeding. However they are easier to count if the ovary is fixed in a tissue hardening preservative and sectioned.

Once the eggs are in the uterus and have been fertilised by sperm from the male, they start to divide. Each grows into a ball of cells, and this early stage of the embryo (a blastocyst) embeds into the wall of the uterus. The uterus itself has enlarged by this stage and the walls have become thickened. If you look at the outside you can see round swellings where the embryos are. When these are dissected out you find the developing embryo inside a fluid filled sac with a large band of opaque tissue running round the middle. This is applied to a similar band in the wall of the uterus to form the placenta, where the vixen's and the embryos' blood supplies come into contact with each other. Oxygen and nutrients pass across from the mother's bloodstream to the developing cub, and carbon dioxide and other wastes go in the other direction.

Gestation (the time that the embryo takes to develop from fertilisation to birth) lasts about 52 days. After birth the uterus starts to shrink and blood in the remains of the placenta breaks down to a black pigment. The result is a dark, cylindrical scar which can be seen in the uterus wall right through to the next breeding season. When you cut open such a uterus, if the vixen has given birth during the last breeding season, you can see a set of these 'placental scars' spaced out along the uterus walls. They are usually all of the same colour intensity, but sometimes you find one that is lighter than the rest. It is tempting to think that this represents an embryo that died early on in development and was therefore not born into the litter. Whether this is the case or not is the sort of thing biologists are inclined to argue about, but studies of the reproduction of foxes in fur farms suggests that it is a reasonable assumption.

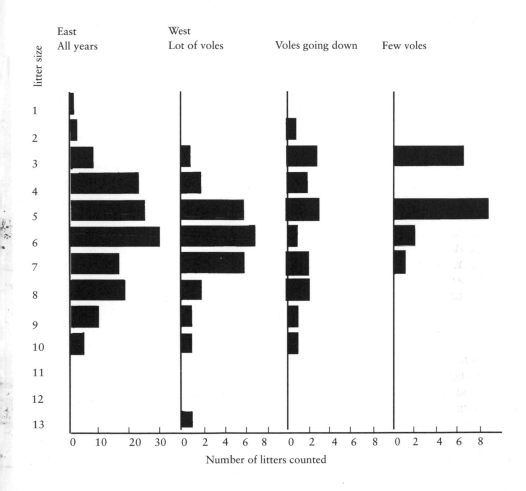

Estimated litter sizes of vixens in the east of Scotland where foxes live mainly on rabbits and birds, and over three successive years in the west of Scotland, where the main winter food is short-tailed voles, which go through cyclical population changes.

When you rely on other people to supply carcases for you they generally appear during the two main periods of fox control – in the spring when vixens are denning, and during the autumn and winter when animals are going about their normal activities. If you are trying to reconstruct the breeding season from dead foxes then you have to deal with samples from right across this time. You might think that the best information would come from counting embryos in pregnant vixens. However relatively few of these are caught and the most heavily pregnant vixens, and particularly those carrying large litters, are probably more wary and less mobile, and may be under represented. Counting placental scars gives a more accurate idea of litter sizes in different years and places. Both the corpora lutea and the scars fade with time but the scars at least are generally visible through the autumn and winter so that information on breeding can be obtained from vixens caught at most times of the year.

Litter size in rural foxes can vary a great deal (although if you ask game-keepers what size a litter of cubs was they always say 'five'). The smallest that I have come across (excluding vixens that fail to breed at all) was one. The largest number of placental scars in one vixen that I have seen (and the largest recorded in the UK) was thirteen. This may not mean that thirteen live cubs were produced and one can ask whether a fox is capable of

Vixen suckling cubs.

rearing a litter of this size. The answer is that it depends on the food supply. This particular litter was conceived in a forested part of western Scotland during a year in which short-tailed vole populations were at a peak, suggesting that, in part at least, litter sizes are related to the amount of food available. Arctic foxes, which are, on average, smaller than red foxes, can produce litters of up to twenty cubs in years when their main prey, lemmings, are abundant. When the lemming population crashes they may not breed at all. A similar but less dramatic situation is found in areas where red foxes have short-tailed voles as their main winter prey. For instance, in western Scotland over three years from 1974 to 1976 during which the vole population declined, the average fox litter size dropped from 6.3 to 4.6 (for those who are not statistically minded, you can't actually have one third of a cub. This is just a convenient way of using and comparing figures. One could say that 100 vixens produced 630 or 460 cubs).

An interesting point to note is that most of this variation in the number of embryos implanted and hence in litter size is already reflected in the number of corpora lutea and therefore in the number of eggs that were originally produced. For instance in the extremes of one and thirteen placental scars described above, the number of corpora lutea were two and sixteen. Therefore most of the individual and annual variation in the number of cubs produced has already been determined during the winter and early spring before reproduction starts. This must be due to each vixen reacting to overwintering vole numbers which are highest before a year of peak population. While some of the differences between years and habitats can be ascribed to changes in the food supply, variation between individuals is much more difficult to explain.

In general in the south of England and Wales litter sizes average around four or five cubs. Apart from food, one of the other main factors limiting reproduction is social behaviour. In dense, settled fox populations where there is little human control, the litter size concentrates at around four cubs. Further reductions in output are due to an increasingly larger proportion of the vixens, usually the younger ones, failing to breed. Conversely in heavily controlled populations, where density is low, average litter sizes can be much larger. In north-east Scotland there has always been a lot of fox control, to the extent the species was locally exterminated in some places. Although control is still carried out, it is less intense than in the past and over the last thirty years the population has been expanding back into areas where it had been absent for up to 150 years. There are therefore fewer food or social restrictions on breeding and litter sizes average up to six or seven cubs in most years.

Go forth and multiply

Adult dogs and vixens reach the peak of their breeding condition in the middle of winter which is when mating occurs. Dogs have a season just as much as vixens. During the summer their testes shrink to cashew-nut size but have regrown to resemble a small walnut by January (it's this kind of precise measurement that makes science such a powerful method of analysis). Most matings take place around the end of January but there is quite a large spread in the breeding season. The only way you can find this out is by estimating backwards from the size of embryos and cubs. Individual foxes can be up to two months apart in their stage of reproduction and mating occurs any time between the beginning of January and the start of March. There are also odd stories of foxes breeding at other times of year but if this does occur it is very rare. There are regional differences as well. For instance the breeding season of foxes in the west of Scotland is on average a fortnight later than in the east. This is probably due to the greater seasonality of the food supply in the west where foxes are largely dependant on voles and a late lambing season. There is also a general trend for foxes from more northerly populations to breed later than those from the south. The differences are small in Britain and can only really be seen when comparing samples of foxes from widely different latitudes in Europe.

Vixen screaming.

New-born cub: note ears folded forward, toes and nails perfectly formed, but no fur yet, and eyes closed.

Cubs are born in March and April. They are about 15 centimetres (5.9 inches) long and weigh around 100 grams (3.5 oz). They are covered in a short, fluffy dark grey fur and have dark ears and a white tip to the tail. Their eyes are closed to start with and open in the second week. They begin to be weaned at three weeks and are generally eating solid food at four. To start with they are fed on regurgitated food by the vixen. Where population density is high and there is more than one vixen in a territory they may co-operate in the rearing of a litter. In areas where there is a lot of control the breeding unit is usually just one dog and a vixen. It is some-times suggested that the dog fox is not much concerned with the litter but as the cubs grow the dog seems to help in supplying food. In hill areas both can be shot when they visit the den. Some shepherds say that when the vixen and cubs are killed the dog goes on some kind of killing spree as if in revenge at the loss of his family. What is probably happening is that the dog fox is still bringing back food for a while but since there is no litter to receive it the behaviour starts to become disorientated. Prey that would otherwise have been eaten by the cubs is dumped instead and you find voles and lambs lying about in odd places near the den.

The kinds of foods that you find in the stomachs of cubs in any particular area are not much different from those that the adults are eating. However there is a tendency for bigger items such as rabbits, game birds and lambs to be commoner, presumably because it is more efficient for the adults to carry these back to the den. By five or six weeks the cubs have grown a sandy, reddish coat to replace their grey one. During this time they may have been moved around between several dens by the vixen. The cubs grow quite fast and most have reached a near adult size by August, although they are still quite skinny and continue to put on weight for the

Cub at three weeks: dark chocolate or grey colour.

next few months. Even though foxes end up a different size in different parts of the country, the average growth rate of cubs in different regions is the same irrespective of whether they are being fed on rabbits and grouse or voles and lambs. The cubs gradually become independent of the family during the summer. There is no evidence that the parents do much to teach them what to eat or how to hunt, although the kinds of food that they were brought up on may have some influence on what they choose to eat later on.

From September onwards the almost fully grown young adult foxes leave the ranges they were born in and disperse to new territories. They

A month to five weeks old, and still blue-eyed.

Cubs outside earth at six weeks old.

are particularly vulnerable at this time and many of the foxes that are killed during this period are less than a year old. Most of the information on dispersal has been got by ear tagging litters of cubs and then recovering the tags later on when the foxes are recaught or killed somewhere else. More detailed information on small samples of animals has also been obtained by following radio-collared foxes for as long as possible. Which animals disperse and how far they go is extremely variable. In general dog foxes are more likely to leave than vixens, do so earlier and tend to move farther. In high density fox populations the maximum distances moved may only be a few kilometres and many foxes are recovered on or next to the home range on which they were born. In hill areas where the density is much lower more foxes disperse and they move much longer distances. The maximum distance recorded in Britain was a dog fox in central Wales that was marked by Gwyn Lloyd. It was recaught 52 kilometres (32 miles) away from its birth place. On average in the same area dog foxes moved about 14 kilometres (9 miles) from their rearing dens to where they were killed and vixens only 2 kilometres (about a mile). Even this is peanuts compared to some red foxes in North America where movements over 100 kilometres (61 miles) are not uncommon. The distance record there for a fox is 394 kilometres (246 miles) for a dog that was marked in Wisconsin and recaught nine months later in Indiana.

Cub at four to five months old.

The Foxtrot

The foxtrot is a popular couple dance that appeared in the United States in 1914. It combined a series of smooth sliding and quicker trotting steps. It was one of a sequence of ragtime dances with animal names such as the Fishwalk, the Turkey Trot and the Bunny Hug. The name was probably second hand, coming from a description of a gait in trotting horses. Originally the dance was freeform and boisterous. During the First World War it was introduced into England. The establishment here regarded it as freakish and indelicate, but it was too popular to ban, so a conference was held in 1920 to try and make it more suitable for genteel ballrooms. It was slowed down and the steps refined and standardised.

Shortly afterwards the Americans fought back and tried to jive it up again. However the British weren't to be defeated so easily and this new derivative of the foxtrot was diverted to become the Quickstep. The English Foxtrot went on to become one of the world's most popular ballroom dances. Despite being  *streamlined, the Foxtrot still retains some semblance of the original syncopated style with the rhythm of the dance, in groups of three bars, cutting across the music in common time. This pattern was made famous in the immortal words of Victor Sylvester (or was it Henry Hall?):*

Slow, Slow, Quick, Quick, Slow

although it should really be:

$\frac{4}{4}$ ♩♩ ♩♩ ♩ ♩ ♩♩ ♩♩ ♩ ♩

   slow   slow   quick   quick slow   slow   quick   quick

Hunting quotes

One knows so well the popular idea of health. The English country gentleman galloping after a fox – the unspeakable in full pursuit of the uneatable.

Oscar Wilde A Woman of No Importance

If my body come from brutes, my soul uncertain, or a fable,
Why not bask amid the senses while the sun of morning shines,
I, the finer brute, rejoicing in my hounds and in my stable,

Alfred Lord Tennyson By An Evolutionist

There is a passion for hunting something deeply implanted in the human breast.

Charles Dickens Oliver Twist

It is very strange, and very melancholy, that the paucity of human pleasures should persuade us ever to call hunting one of them.

Samuel Johnson Johnsonian Memoirs

'Unting is all that's worth living for – all time is lost wot is not spent in 'unting – it is like the hair we breathe – if we have it not we die – it's the sport of kings, the image of war without its guilt, and only five-and-twenty per cent of its danger.

Robert Smith Surtees Handley Cross

Detested sport, that owes its pleasures to another's pain.

William Cowper The Task

Foxes often backtrack and hounds are oblivious (after 18th century print).

The fox, when caught, is worth nothing: he is followed for the pleasure of following,

> *Sydney Smith* Lady S. Holland's Memoir

It arn't that I love the fox less, but that I loves the hounds more.

> *Robert Smith Surtees* Handley Cross

The world may be divided into people that read, people that write, people that think, and fox hunters.

> *William Shenstone* On Writing And Books

It isn't mere convention. Everyone can see that the people who hunt are the right people and the people who don't are the wrong ones.

> *George Bernard Shaw* Heartbreak House

Hunting people tend to be church goers on a higher level than ordinary folk. One has a religious experience in the field.

> *Christopher Seal* Letter to The Times

Everyone has observed how much more dogs are animated when they hunt in a pack, than when they pursue their game apart. We might, perhaps, be at a loss to explain this phenomenon, if we had not experience of a similar in ourselves.

David Hume A Treatise of Human Nature

No sportsman wants to kill the fox or the pheasant as I want to kill him when I see him doing it.

George Bernard Shaw

For what were all these country patriots born?
To hunt, and vote and raise the price of corn?

Lord Byron

Refortified by exercise and air,
I, jogging home astride my chestnut mare,
Grow half humane, and question the propriety,
Of foxes torn to bits in smart society.

Siegfried Sassoon

For I looked into its pages and I read the book of fate,
And saw Fox Hunting abolished by an order of the state.

W. Bromley Davenport Lowesby Hall

The unspeakable in pursuit of the uneatable

Quotations on fox hunting, whether they be heartfelt opinions or sayings put in the mouth of characters in plays or novels, encapsulate the range of attitudes on the subject. They vary from delight in the sport to execration at the fate of the fox. In between are comments on the social status of fox hunters or observations that there might be more profitable ways of spending one's spare time than hunting. Oscar Wilde's is probably the most famous but this is not so much pro-fox as anti-establishment. Few of the quotations are recent, suggesting that there are no 'modern' attitudes to hunting. If anything has changed it is their distribution within society as population patterns and recreational interests have developed through the centuries. The fact that so many quotations can be found is a reflection of how deeply fox hunting has become embedded in the English psyche. There are no *bon mots* by Oscar Wilde on ferreting, or acerbic comments by George Bernard Shaw on coarse fishing. Obviously several score or more of people on horseback, dressed in loud costumes, shouting and blowing horns, and galloping across the countryside after a pack of baying hounds, are liable to attract attention. However fox hunting goes much deeper than this and is bound up with the social structure of rural communities and the pattern of land ownership in England over the past few hundred years.

Mounted hunters following packs of hounds after a variety of quarry is something that originated far back in European history. At one time the art of *Venery* (everything to do with the codes and practice of high class hunting) was balanced against the parallel enterprise of *Chivalry* (everything to do with knightly conduct in love and war). One of the problems of being royalty or nobility in the past, when these kinds of things were taken seriously, was that, except during periods of war, it was not a full time job. There were large amounts of spare time to be filled in and much of this was spent in hunting. In the Middle Ages large parts of Britain and Europe were set aside as Royal Forests. These were not always forests as such, any more than deer forests in Scotland today actually contain any trees, but were areas where the King had exclusive hunting rights, principally for deer. Anybody trying to interfere with this prerogative was likely

to end up viewing the rest of their shortened life span from a local gibbet.

Under a feudal system all land was owned by the monarch and was let as He or She saw fit to those who were of service. Much of the history of England, from Magna Carta onwards, has consisted of the nobility trying, and succeeding, in diverting power and land from the Crown and parcelling it up between themselves. Agricultural improvements during the 17th and 18th centuries made possession of land more profitable. Large tracts were brought into private ownership, enclosed with hedges and fences, and amalgamated into the estates that are still a feature of much of the British countryside. Overseeing this was a layer of rural landlords ranging from dukes to squires. Underneath them were tenant farmers and their employees who did the actual work and who were therefore, by definition, not gentlemen. The gentlemen, meanwhile, having the time and money and owning the land, wished to cement their status by indulging in 'The Sport of Kings'. Unfortunately (for them) intensive agriculture and deer forests don't mix so they had to find something else to chase. After experimenting with hares they discovered that the commonest remaining large animal that would run any distance in front of hounds was the fox.

By the 18th century hunting to hounds had become the most popular gentleman's recreation. Hunting countries (this is the technical term for the territory of a hunt, defended or not) could be very large and, while some people were quite happy to ride where they wanted, the whole enterprise functioned better if the local farmers were drawn into it. In some cases this was achieved by putting clauses in the lease that allowed hunts to pass and outlawed the killing of foxes by any other means. During the Georgian period, when new riding techniques were introduced, hunting in the English Midlands was mainly seen as an aristocratic pursuit and acquired a poor image, with hard drinking, hard riding Regency bucks tearing up the countryside. Indirectly the French managed to change that. The rigid social distinctions between the classes on the Continent and the alienation of aristocrats from their estates were seen as leading to such horrors as the French Revolution. In England, egalitarianism in the hunting field was promoted as a way of uniting the classes and maintaining social stability. Since then fox hunting has always prided itself that anybody can take part provided that they had a horse and didn't make a nuisance of themselves. Naturally there has always been a limit on the degree of fraternisation and the fact that somebody rode to hounds didn't necessarily mean that they need be invited to the hunt ball. There is some parallel here with the English concept of amateurism. Anybody could take part in a sport, provided that they had sufficient money and spare time to be able to participate. The Napoleonic Wars further embedded fox hunting into society. While a few thought it was something that should be dispensed with during a period of national crisis, the more popular view was to applaud hunting as a symbol of the national spirit. It encouraged horsemanship and the breeding of superior horses for what was, after all, something that was not a lot different from a cavalry charge. The standard dress of scarlet coats came from the practice of army officers of the period on leave wearing their uniform in the field. These used to be called 'hunting pink' after a Mr Pink who was supposed to be a fashionable tailor in London (good job his name wasn't Mr Green). The army used a different tailor and remained as Redcoats, not Pinkcoats. The popularity of hunting among army officers led to it being spread around the world in the train of the Empire. Where foxes were rare or absent, as in India and Africa, they chased local animals such as jackals instead. There is still one hunt left in India, the Ootacamund, although it claims not to kill anything.

Fox hunting came to be seen as one of the linchpins of rural life. While the actual number of people taking part in any one hunt was quite small, the paternalistic spirit of the whole enterprise was extended to farm tenants, hunt servants and the patronising of most of the inns within range of the kennels. The practice of younger sons of landed families going into the church led to the phenomenon of 'Hunting Parsons', exponents of muscular Christianity, some of whom spent more time out badger digging than in the pulpit. The most famous of these was Parson Jack Russell, who developed one form of what is now recognised as a breed of terriers. In Victorian times, with the introduction of railways, which enabled townspeople to travel to the Shires, and the rise of members of the middle classes who wished to improve their social tone, hunting became further expanded. Nobody questioned the fact that hunts were run from the top down and the more exclusive 'smart packs' could freeze out people that they didn't want, but there were plenty of 'scratch packs' that anybody could join, as satirised by the writer R. S. Surtees in the character of 'John Jorrocks of Great Coram Street, Grocer and Tea Dealer of St Botolph's Lane in the City of London'.

As with anything that aspires to cult status, fox hunting is crammed with rituals and jargon. The sport's high profile has led to many of these entering general speech. Words and phrases related to hunting are more widespread than most people realise. For instance 'The Whip's Office' in our great Mother of Parliaments comes from the job of whipper-in to a pack of hounds. The description 'fast lady' stems from the mistresses of fox hunters and high class prostitutes who were the first women to take to the hunting field in the Georgian era, when 'fast' hunting was introduced. They were gradually squeezed out as respectability gained the upper hand during Victorian times. The slang word 'berk' (meaning somebody who is only 75p in the £) comes from that estimable organisation 'The Berkshire Hunt', which in turn is Cockney rhyming slang for something that escapes me for the moment.

Yoiks tally-ho, etc.

Originally hunting was a slow procedure in which the hounds walked along with their noses glued to the ground. Modern fox hunting started in Leicestershire in the 1750s. The then Master of the Quorn, one Hugo Meynell, decided that hunting as practised up to then was too boring. He imported hounds from various places and bred stronger, faster packs, turning it into the all galloping, all jumping exercise that it is today.

There are certain basic ingredients to a hunt. Firstly there has to be a Master, who is often the biggest local landowner or the person prepared to sink most money into the enterprise. The Master is partly a figurehead but is also responsible for the overall social and financial organisation of the hunt, nowadays with a committee. Technically nobody else hunts except at His (or nowadays in some cases Her) invitation. Next there is a professional Huntsman who is responsible for the hounds and the management of the kennel. He is generally assisted by two Whippers-in who help to manage the pack and the kennels. In the field the first Whipper-in is responsible for seeing when the fox breaks cover (emerges into the open) and alerting the Huntsman with a 'halloo', who then sets the hounds on. The second Whipper-in helps the Huntsman keep the pack together. Other sundry dogsbodies such as terrier men, earth stoppers and fence repairers may work on a part time or voluntary basis. A typical pack consists of sixteen and a half couple of hounds but in order to supply this number several days a week the whole kennel can contain sixty couple of hounds or more (British field sports enthusiasts like to count things in twos – foxes, pheasants and grouse in braces and hounds in couples – possibly because two is a convenient handful).

The purpose of a hunt is to chase a fox for as long a distance as possible and then kill it. Once an area has been chosen for hunting because foxes are thought to be there, most of the known earths are stopped during the previous night to prevent the fox going to ground too soon. Once the field and the pack has met, the hounds are allowed into a likely patch of gorse or scrub to try and scare out a fox. This is known as drawing cover (usually spelt 'covert' but generally still pronounced 'cover'). Fox hunting is full of such jargon which has become incorporated into the rituals of the sport. Some of these words, such as 'tally-ho', are derived from earlier French deer hunting cries. Once the hounds scent or see a fox they give tongue and start following it. They are given a short head start so that there is no danger of them being overridden by the horses, and then the chase starts in earnest. When following scent alone the hunt is fairly slow, but once the hounds get near the fox or catch sight of it, everything speeds up. If they lose the scent, the Huntsman gets them organised to cast around and pick it up again. The hunt ends when the fox is either lost, goes to ground and is bolted by terriers or dug out and shot by the Huntsman, or the hounds catch it and kill it themselves. The hunting season starts in September and October with cub hunting. This is mainly a private affair for the Huntsman to train hounds and to encourage some young foxes to disperse from their breeding areas so that they are spread more around the country. The main hunting season lasts for the next five months during the winter.

When the new fast hunting came in it meant that more chases and kills could be fitted into a day. This increased pressure on local fox populations and various ploys were devised to make sure that there were always foxes available. The most general of these was to modify the habitat by planting patches of gorse and small woods for foxes to lie up in. Some people also promoted the construction of artificial earths to encourage immigrant foxes to stay. Although often frowned on, the next step was to 'turn down' foxes. This involved catching adult foxes or cubs in one place, feeding them up and releasing them in the hunt country before the season started so that they became reasonably established. Some people made a living stealing foxes from one hunt and selling them to another. The more legitimate method was to buy litters off gamekeepers who were trying to protect pheasant shoots or grouse moors, and who would otherwise have killed them. These litters were kept in captivity for as short a time as possible to stop them becoming tame, and then put into a convenient empty earth or rabbit burrow. They were fenced in for a few days and fed with any game which came to hand. The fence was then removed but feeding continued until it was sure that they had taken up residence. The extreme method of guaranteeing a hunt was to use a 'bag' fox. This was a fox that had been caught and kept in captivity, and which was released directly into the cover in front of the hounds. These did not usually provide a good scent and sometimes were doctored by having their pads slashed, or by being doused in aniseed. However, not all bag foxes were killed. Some were dug out and used again. There was a hunt in Devon in the 1820s, composed of dwarf hounds that were trained not to attack the fox. One particular fox, called the 'Bold Dragoon', was hunted thirty-six times in one season. These practices are no longer accepted as a part of the sport, although some claim that they still occasionally go on.

The hunted fox sometimes puts up a fresh one.

The alternative to using a live fox is 'drag hunting'. This requires a runner who creates a scent by dragging a bag soaked in fox urine or aniseed over the ground for three or four miles at a time. There have been specialist packs of draghounds, but these were generally for sportsmen who could only hunt at weekends or on odd days when they wanted to make sure that they had something to chase. Drag hunting has never been popular among most fox hunters. Various reasons are given for this. One is that there is no variety or unpredictablity to it. The field just goes hell-for-leather and then stops. The whole exercise is seen as artificial and there is no climax which the killing of a fox provides. Many huntsmen believe that the hounds need to have live quarry to kill in order to maintain their motivation. This is along the lines of some greyhound trainers who set their dogs onto a rabbit occasionally in order to remind them what the whole exercise is supposed to be about.

The indefatigable in pursuit of the unenviable

The only huntsman that most people have ever heard of is John Peel ('with his coat so gray...'), mainly because somebody wrote a popular song about him. He lived between 1777 and 1854 and hunted the Derwentwater and Skiddaw area of Cumberland for more than fifty years. However, unlike those dealt with so far, he spent most of his time on his feet, because a lot of Cumberland is too rough and steep to gallop over on horseback. The hunt that he ran is generally referred to as a foot pack to distinguish it from mounted hunts. Rightly or wrongly, most hill farmers regard the fox as a pest and foot packs are seen mainly as a form of fox control in a landscape where other techniques are difficult. This is not to say that they aren't also a sport. Peel chased hares as well as foxes, and seems to have spent two days in the pub for every one day out hunting (he probably needed the rest).

In areas with mounted hunts the majority of foxes that are killed are caught by the hounds. In hill country the fox has more opportunity to go to ground. There is no stopping of earths, partly because the chase is not the prime object, but mainly because a lot of them are in inaccessible rock piles. Because of this, different breeds of terrier are required. Variously called Lakeland, Patterdale or Fell terriers, they are long legged, strongly built dogs that are capable of following the hounds up hills, and are then able to go to ground and kill the fox unaided. This is a tough business. Not only is the country hard going, but the foxes are larger than in the lowlands and are capable of putting up a bigger fight. Over the years many terriers have disappeared into piles of rocks and have never been seen again.

While Cumberland is the natural home of these hunts, they have been exported to central Wales, and in the last twenty years three of them have been set up in the Highlands of Scotland. Like all Fox Destruction Societies in Scotland these still receive a 50 percent Government grant, as opposed to England and Wales where money for that sort of thing was stopped in 1979. Keeping a pack of hounds and a huntsman going throughout the year is the most expensive form of fox control. The farmers are pleased because the hunt is always on call should a problem arise, although there

Anyone at home?

is also the occasional danger in rough country that a hound will decide to 'go native' and start eating sheep on its own account. However, once you've got a pack you have to keep them working and the rest of the season is spent on general fox control to try and reduce the overall population. There is no evidence that such mass control is of any real benefit to anybody but it is seen as part of the process of dealing with a pest. Once an animal has been classified in people's minds as a pest or vermin then a whole range of attitudes become acceptable. Most people will happily condone the merciless poisoning of rats (with very unpleasant and inhumane chemicals) because they don't like them, they think that they might do something nasty or because they once heard about Bubonic plague, rather than to get rid of a particular rat that has been proved beyond reasonable doubt to have done some damage. Many hill farmers have a similiar attitude towards the fox.

Is fox hunting wrong?

Arguments about the ethics of killing animals for sport go back a long way and in their modern form are descended from the Utilitarian philosophers of the 18th century. The pejorative use of the term 'blood sport' originated in the 1890s. While all field sports involve killing animals in various ways, the idea of setting dogs onto quarry seems to evoke particularly strong feelings in some people, even though many of them probably have pet cats which are free to decimate the local bird population with impunity. It is often said of those with a puritanical bent that it is not so much the doing of something that upsets them but the fact that anybody else should get enjoyment out of it. When it comes to fox hunting the situation is complicated even more by social and political attitudes to those who participate in it.

At its most basic, hunting used to be about procuring animals for food or to use their skins for clothing. Morally, a distinction can be made between killing an animal in order to eat it, and chasing and killing just for the sport of it. However for as long as there have been human societies there has also been a trophy element to hunting with some people trying to express their power, status or self esteem by killing more or bigger animals than others. To those with a 'Great White Hunter' self image shooting a lion has always been more important that shooting a rabbit, even though the only thing you can do with a lion is have it stuffed and leave it in the hall for the moths to eat. In the 18th century killing a fox was as important as chasing it, and there was a repertoire of atavistic behaviours associated with the death, such as smearing people with blood on their first day out, cutting off the fox's mask, pads and brush, and exhibiting it in a tree before throwing the remains to the hounds. With time these rituals were downplayed and the chase itself has now come to be seen as the most important thing.

The debate about fox hunting and other blood sports comes from a clash between pragmatic and idealist subcultures. At one extreme are those who find personal enjoyment in many aspects of a field sport and who are completely indifferent to any physical suffering that they may be inflicting on the animal concerned. At the other, there are those who so completely identify with the animal that they imagine that it is suffering all of the feelings and thoughts that they think they would undergo in a similiar situation. Some may question whether it is 'sporting' to block an animal's

Foxes frequently outwit hounds.

escape route by stopping earths so that it is chased to exhaustion. Hunters will reply that only about 25% of foxes hunted are actually killed. The rest get away, although they may be hunted again another day. In addition the concept of 'sportsmanship' is something that is generally agreed amongst those taking part in a sport, rather than being imposed by outsiders.

Justifications for fox hunting have changed through the centuries. At first, it was regarded as a healthy recreation for gentlemen, which kept them on their estates and away from the vices of the city. Then it became a training for war. Nowadays various defences are put up.

Firstly the tradition and pageantry surrounding hunting are presented as a defining and economically important aspect of English country life. At the last count there were about two hundred hunts on the British mainland, most of them mounted. Around fifty thousand people are said to take part in hunts in one way or another, and hunting may affect the incomes of up to two hundred thousand. Since hunting is an expensive business this relatively small number injects many millions of pounds into the rural economy. If hunting stopped, not only would this income disappear, but many of the skills associated with horses, dogs, dress and gear would go with it. The argument put against this is that tradition in itself is not a defence since there have been 'entertainments' in the past such as bull and bear baiting, and cock and dog fighting, which were banned as long ago as 1835. Admittedly we now see these as being of an extra order of magnitude in that they depended solely on the exhibition of violence for their popularity, but this was not necessarily the way that they were regarded at the time. Fox hunting only survived because of its social status. As Sidney Smith said in 1809 'A man of ten thousand a year may worry a fox as much as he pleases, and a poor labourer is carried before a magistrate for paying sixpence to see an exhibition of courage between a dog and a bear'.

Secondly, hunting is now advanced as a method of fox control. It is argued that foxes need controlling and that if the hunt didn't do it, then farmers would, using even less humane methods such as snaring or illegal methods such as poisoning. It has been estimated that hunts kill between 10,000 and 20,000 foxes a year. This is probably less than 10 percent of the British fox population and, since mathematical models show that you have to kill more than 75 percent of all foxes in order to make the population go into decline, the overall impact of fox hunting is almost trivial. However this is not the whole story. Should a particular fox be causing trouble, then the hunt provides a reservoir of experienced and skilled people who can deal with it. The problem with this is that most of the demands for fox control come from sheep farmers in upland areas where mounted hunts don't operate. The main reason for fox control in lowland areas is in game preservation where keepers are already employed to do the job. You then have to decide whether their methods, principally snaring, are more or less humane than hunting. The whole idea that hunting is a method of fox control has to be regarded with some suspicion, coming as it does from the fraternity that invented the crime of 'vulpicide'. Not only that but serious fox control is done during the denning season by which time hunting has stopped to allow the fox population to recover for the next winter. And, as we have seen from the history of hunting, hunts have gone to great lengths to structure farmland and provide artificial earths in order to encourage foxes rather than reduce them.

Those who have observed hunted foxes say that they appear unconcerned by much of the chase and only react during the last few moments when the hounds are directly on top of them. As one old huntsman said, 'foxes die very game', which means that they face up to the hounds and don't make a fuss during the brief struggle. The idea of foxes shrieking as they are torn apart by dogs is almost entirely propagandist. As we have already seen, foxes are not prone to display their emotions, so it is

Sleeping foxes, like sitting birds, give off no scent.

difficult to say much about their internal state when being attacked by dogs. However, the speed of the operation combined with the deadening physiological effects of shock probably mean that the fox does not feel a great deal while being killed. Dogs in general, and especially in packs, are efficient killers and don't fool around in the way that cats are inclined to do (the exception to this is lowland terriers which have been bred to stand off and worry their quarry so as to make it bolt, or so that those above ground can hear their barking and know where to start digging). Much is made in some quarters of the fox being torn apart by the hounds. This happens after the fox is dead, and while it may be unpleasant to the disinterested observer, bears little relevance to the issue of humaneness. Pictures of an animal that has been squashed on the road will elicit similar feelings. Few, if any, wild animals live out their potential life span and they don't die in bed with their relatives standing round clutching handkerchieves. What is better for the fox? A fairly rapid death from the bite of a hound or a more lingering one from distemper or some other natural controlling agent.

Hunting is quite a dangerous sport. Many of those who criticised it for cruelty in the 19th century were more concerned about the effects on the horses and hounds rather than the fox, just as some people protest about steeplechasing nowadays. Death and injury among the riders has always been notable, although more so in the past when it was the fashion to wear top hats in the field. A not inconsiderable number have inherited after a landed relative has landed on his or her head. If it is of any consolation to anybody, fox hunters are as callous about each other as they are about the fox, and anybody falling off and injuring themselves is supposed to put up with it and not interfere with the rest of the hunt.

So is fox hunting wrong? There isn't an answer to this question. Most people's attitudes to hunting are based more than anything else on emotional reactions to something that they are either unfamiliar with or which they have been brought up to regard as a part of normal life. Added to this there is a small minority of 'anti' activists who are pursuing their own personal or political agendas. Whether fox hunting survives or not is as much down to fashion as to absolute values. The majority of the British population is against hunting, but this may partly be a reflection of the fact that most people live in cities. To the pragmatist much of what goes on in field sports is no different from the hurly-burly of the natural world where animals of all degrees of sensibility are shredded and gobbled minute by minute. To the idealist there is somewhere a perfect world in which pain and suffering has come to an end. Most people are somewhere in between.

In fact the practical and legal restraints on hunting have increased over the years. This started with the introduction of barbed wire to replace hedges and the selling off of parts of large estates. It continued with such things as the planting of winter cereals, which increased the amount of ploughed ground during the hunting season, and the construction of motorways, which cut countries up into small sections. To assuage public opinion, hunts have agreed among themselves that foxes which have gone to ground should either be left or dug out and humanely killed, and should not be bolted just to carry on the chase. Legal protection for badgers has complicated the practice of stopping earths as foxes may take up residence or hide temporarily in old setts. Badger setts cannot be damaged or dug into, so that if they are to be stopped to prevent them being used by a fox, only a light packing such as hay, bracken or paper sacks can be put into the entrance. It is possible in the future that further constraints will be put on the use of terriers.

With dog and gun

During the middle of the 19th century, with the development of the modern shotgun, in some places shooting started to outclass fox hunting as the most fashionable field sport. While the prime object of fox hunters was to protect the fox for the chase, one of the main functions of gamekeepers in charge of shoots was to eliminate foxes (and all other predators) from their beats in order to protect gamebirds. This became one of the classic sources of conflict in country districts, second only to that between gamekeepers and farmers over rabbits.

Many of the attitudes and some of the practices of gamekeepers today are not much different to 150 years ago. This can be seen from one angle as a commendable attachment to tradition or from another as an ingrained conservatism. Their main job is to produce the maximum number of birds for shooting and they object to anything that tries to interfere with this. Some views on the role of predation were established early on. Charles Darwin said in *The Origin of Species* in 1859, 'there seems to be little doubt that the stock of partridges, grouse, and hares on any large estate depends chiefly on the destruction of vermin'. Since Darwin's time ecologists have argued among themselves as to the role of predators in limiting or controlling prey populations and at times fashionable theories have outweighed whatever evidence was available (so you thought that scientists were objective, eh?).

One of the dominant theories for a while was that the breeding density of herbivore populations was determined by a variety of primary (i.e. food) or intrinsic factors (for instance, social behaviour) and that this produced a supply of individuals which were surplus to the numbers that the habitat could support. These were doomed to die in one way or another and some or all of them might be eaten by predators which therefore had no effect on the main prey population. Naturally the world is a complex place and there are some situations where this theory might fit. It applies particularly well to the human exploitation of fish and foxes provided the numbers killed remain below the optimum breeding capacity of the population (which is nowadays the case with foxes but no longer with fish). There are two complications when you apply these ideas to game birds. Firstly the set-up is artificial because strenuous efforts are made to maintain these bird populations at a higher level than they would achieve if left to themselves. This is taken to extremes with quarry like pheasants which are reared in large numbers in captivity and then released into the country-side. For a predator such as the fox that can switch between a lot of different prey species as they change in availability this local superabundance of food is an obvious attraction. Secondly shooters are themselves essentially predators on the game bird population and so are competing with the other predators for the surplus that has been specially created.

There have been a number of experiments in Europe and America in recent years which have shown that if predators are rigorously controlled then populations of ground-nesting birds, ducks and other species such as hares, increase, sometimes doubling in numbers. The theory outlined above of an exploitable surplus only applies once the prey population has bred and there are enough individuals about to distinguish between potential breeders and surplus. If predators attack breeding individuals directly then they have a capacity to reduce the prey population quite easily. It is prob-ably no coincidence that the commonest predators and scavengers in the countryside today, such as foxes, crows and magpies, are also the most succesful finders and destroyers of nests. Loss of partridge nests can aver-age over fifty percent a year and much of this is due to foxes.

Obviously to anybody who dislikes the shooting of birds for sport in the first place, killing foxes and other predators in order to stop them eating game is not seen as a square deal. Where and when foxes should be con-trolled depends in part on what role you think game preservation has in the environment. There is also a balance to be considered between the maintenance of semi-natural game bird populations such as red grouse which rely very heavily on habitat management for their existence, and the kind of put-and-take shoot where penfuls of naive pheasant poults are shovelled out into the fields to survive for a few months. Shoots which try and encourage wild breeding stocks of birds are nowadays seen as an im-portant bulwark against the spread of industrialised agriculture or forestry, and the loss of habitat and species diversity that this leads to. While such diversity could be achieved in other, more bureaucratic ways, it is much more reliably done by having a countryside which functions under the control and to the advantage of those who live there. It is also argued that the predator control required for game birds has a knock on effect and encourages the populations of other species, particularly ground-nesting birds. While there is still some argument about this, a number of conserva-tion organisations feel the need to control or somehow limit access by foxes to some of their reserves for the same reason. Over the past two hundred years a great deal of time and money has gone into making large parts of what we now regard as the typical British countryside a fit place

for game to live in. Maintaining these blocks of cover, hedgerows and field margins to their best advantage provides areas that are isolated from the effects of ploughing and agricultural chemicals. This encourages plants and invertebrates that would otherwise be rare or absent on many farms and forms the basis of a complex food web that leads to the presence of more visible vertebrate species in addition to game birds. Most people no longer support the production of maximum bags of birds and the wholescale destruction of ground predators and birds of prey that was part of this system. However, provided that there is a curb on excess, one way of maintaining a diverse countryside without paying farmers not to farm or imposing management regimes on them is to encourage game production. Fox control might have to remain as part of that although there is room for discussion about the methods that should be used.

Engines

People have been catching and killing foxes throughout recorded history and beyond, using any number of methods ranging from poison arrows to rocks suspended on pieces of rope. In modern times the techniques have become more systematised.

During the 19th century one of the mainstays of fox control in gamekeeping areas was the gin trap. The name 'gin' is a corruption of the word 'engine', a term used at one time for any mechanical device. Sprung metal traps of one sort or another have been around since the sixteenth century, but the most common commercial gin trap used for foxes consisted of a flat steel spring which engaged two six-inch, rectangular jaws. These could be toothed, but smoother faces were usually preferred. They also came in smaller versions, a four-inch trap for rabbits and a three-inch for stoats, rats and other smaller fry. These traps were very powerful and most people would need to stand on the spring with their full weight in order to set them. Once set they were not very selective and gin traps and their metal equivalents for birds, pole traps, probably did more than anything else to bring many predators to the verge of extinction in Britain. Despite being strong, these traps were not big enough to kill most animals and were designed to hold them by the lower leg until they died of exhaustion, starvation or somebody came along and despatched them. This kind of trap has always been favoured by those who catch animals for their fur since it does not damage the pelt, and they are still used extensively in places like Canada and Russia for fur trapping. There most trapped animals freeze to death in few hours but in a milder climate a fox might stay held in a trap for a long time. Sometimes the jaws would close over the foot joint and presumably after a lot of struggling, the joint would be cut and the fox escape. Up until about twenty years ago it was still possible to find three legged foxes hopping around.

The gin trap was banned over most of Britain in 1958, but due to complaints about this from sheep farmers in the west of Scotland it could still be legally used there up until 1973 in a 'drowning' or 'island set'. This was made by digging a large doughnut shaped pit which (being in the west of Scotland) immediately filled with water. A peninsular was then built out to the small island in the middle. This was baited with some kind of smelly offal and a gin trap was set on the peninsula attached to a longish chain which was securely staked. The fox, in trying to get at the bait, would put

Wounded fox.

a foot in the trap, fall off the island and, in its struggles, drown. When the gin trap was banned, efforts were made to develop a more humane form of trap for foxes. Many designs were tested but the only one extensively tried was a spring loaded foot snare called the Phelp's Trap. This was based on a similar trap used in North America, and foot snares have also been used in Sweden where neck snaring is illegal. While it was concluded that these caught foxes and were more humane that steel leg-hold traps, they never became accepted. The only places that you will find steel fox traps now are in museums and on pub walls. Wire mesh cage traps have been introduced in recent years but they are little used, being expensive, bulky and easily damaged. Artificial earths have been used for a long time for attracting foxes, and they also have a potential for being turned into traps, something which has not been fully explored.

At present the main legal method of fox control is snaring. This is one of the more ancient methods of catching foxes although in its modern form high tensile steel wires are used. For many years the most commonly used commercial snare was designed to lock around the fox's neck once it had been pulled tight. This was achieved by inserting a small angled plate with

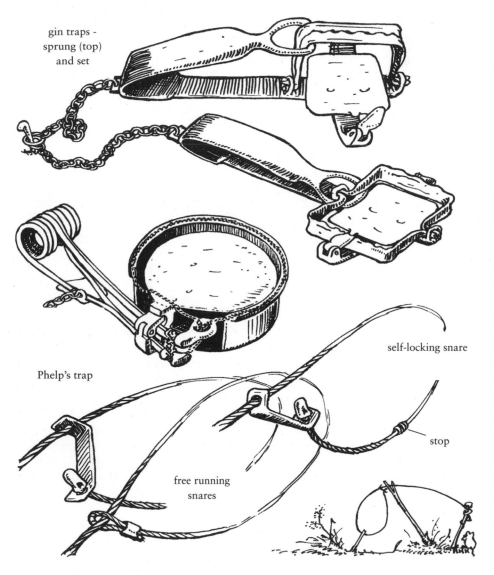

gin traps -
sprung (top)
and set

Phelp's trap

self-locking snare

stop

free running
snares

Traps and snares (not all to the same scale). The locking snare shows a stop which is intended to prevent it closing tight on the foot of a deer or sheep, should it put its foot in.

a couple of holes in it where the eye of the noose would normally be (the presence of a plate doesn't automatically mean that a snare locks – it depends upon the way the plate is set). The fox's struggles would make the plate press against the wire and prevent the noose sliding up. These were made illegal in 1981 and now the only snares allowed are free running ones that do not exert permanent pressure on the fox's neck and throttle it. The snare is set on a trail used by foxes, often near where this passes through a hole in fence or hedge. There are rules for setting snares so that they are more likely to catch foxes than anything else, but this can never be guaranteed. Foxes do not take lightly to being held by the neck and spend many hours thrashing about to try and release themselves. It is still possible to kill a fox with an ordinary snare. Some thoughtful gamekeepers used to set them near a fence or railings so that in its struggles the fox jumped over the barrier and hung itself. Once snares have been set they are supposed to be visited at least once and preferably twice a day, but even with the best intentions foxes are subjected to a considerable amount of suffering. In most other western European countries snaring is illegal and many people in Britain dislike it, but in the absence of an alternative there is considerable pressure from game management interests to keep it as a method of control.

Shooting is used for control in a number of ways. Foxes can be driven out of woods by dogs towards a line of shotguns or bolted from holes by a terrier. In the Highlands some people stay out all night near a den and try and shoot the foxes as they come home at dawn. Keepers may go out with a spotlight at night and try and pick up foxes in a field and shoot them using the shine from their eyes as a target. Some go even further and make noises like a frightened rabbit or cub, which draw curious foxes into range. Shooting may seem like the ideal, clinical method of fox control, but it is only that if a vital target is hit. In Sweden, where shooting is the main method of killing, post mortems on foxes have shown that many have old bullet wounds. The energy of a high velocity bullet is such that even a flesh wound can create a shock wave through the muscle that breaks nearby bones.

Up until 1981 it was legal to gas fox earths with cyanide. During the 1970s cyanide gas was being used to kill badgers in their setts in some parts of England because the population was infected with bovine tuberculosis. However, it was shown that this was inhumane because badgers and other members of the weasel family have a high tolerance to the effects of the gas. Cyanide gassing was banned for all larger mammals (it is still legal to use it for rabbits) although there is no particular evidence that it is inhumane for foxes.

Snared, shot or poisoned.

It has been illegal to poison foxes in most of the UK since the beginning of the century (although up until recently, not in Northern Ireland). This did not stop it becoming fashionable among gamekeepers to do so during the 1960s and 70s. Strychnine has been used for a long time for fox poisoning, to the extent that some shepherds in Scotland used to carry crystals of washing soda around in their pockets. If they saw one of their dogs eat anything on the hill, they would immediately force the soda down the dog's throat in order to make it throw up. Strychnine can be bought under Government licence for poisoning moles, and in the past it was likely that some of this was diverted for killing foxes and crows. Since the 1970s legal restrictions on the sale of such poisons have been much tighter. The most fashionable method of poisoning foxes for a while was to use the insecticide phosdrin (also known by its trade name Mevinphos). This is a highly toxic nerve poison and there were several cases of gamekeepers killing themselves accidentally with it. While a number of people have been charged and convicted of poisoning wildlife over the years, the main limitation has been by restricting the supply of potential materials. The paradox of poisoning is that it is the most effective and, if the right materials are used, one of the more humane methods of killing foxes. Before oral vaccination was developed it was the first choice for serious fox control in the event of a rabies outbreak. The problem with poisoning is that is it usually completely indisciminate in its action, and is as likely to wipe out every other scavenger and carnivore in the area, many of them protected species, as it is to kill foxes.

Does anybody need to kill foxes?

Those who hunt for pleasure do so for a variety of reasons and it cannot be said that they need to kill foxes. Authorities such as the Duke of Beaufort tell us that most of the people in a hunting field never even see the fox so that many participants would probably get much the same excitement out of hunting whether a fox is killed or not. However to a central core of aficionados who have been brought up steeped in the tradition, fox hunting without a fox is a bit like bacon without eggs (if you're a vegetarian you probably don't like fox hunting anyway). Nearly everybody else who kills foxes does it because they regard the animal as a pest. This leads to the 'the only good fox is a dead fox' syndrome. Most shooting estates and control organisations kill foxes routinely throughout the winter and during the denning season. There are still some bounty schemes in existence where people are paid for every brush that they can produce. It is quite possible for one or two keepers on a medium sized shooting estate to kill between 50 and 100 foxes in a year, far more animals than could ever live on the ground that they cover. What they are doing is creating a sink into which foxes in the surrounding area move as the residents are removed. This can be called the traditional approach. It is difficult to come up with reliable figures but it is probable that around 100,000 foxes are killed every year in Britain. The question has to be asked: with modern technologies and new biological methods, could the same ends be achieved using other means which don't involve killing foxes?

The most obvious procedure is to protect whatever it is that you want to keep alive instead. Locking up your ducks and chickens at night is always recommended, although once predators discover that there is food somewhere they can be quite ingenious at getting inside. This sort of total protection can only be applied to small areas. The use of electric fences to keep foxes out of small plots of duck or tern breeding habitat has been effective and has also been tried for small lambing parks. Electric fences require constant supervision and are usually only useful as a short term measure. Some people have tried to scare foxes away from lambing ewes using flashing traffic lamps. One farm recently claimed that they could scare foxes away by playing Radio 4 over loudspeakers at night. Presum-

ably this was because it made the foxes think that there were people about rather than because they didn't like the programmes. Smells can also be used to deter foxes or mask the scent of nesting gamebirds. There are commercial products of considerable vintage such as 'Renardine' which have an unpleasant oily smell and which can repel a number of species. However, foxes are bright animals and it may not take a persistent individual long to discover that some of these things are shams.

More general ideas involve habitat management such as increasing the amount of cover for ground-nesting birds, or providing extra food for predators during sensitive periods so that they don't need to go and look for prey. Experiments have been done to try to train predators away from eating a particular food by leaving examples of it around which have been dosed with a slow acting emetic chemical. This makes the animals sick a few hours after eating and the object of the exercise is to convince the predator that eating something, for instance lambs, is bad for it. These experiments work well in captivity but no one has yet made them successful in the field. Since foxes are territorial it has been suggested that once the original animals have been removed it might be possible to put out scent marks that persuade other foxes that the ground is still occupied so that they keep moving on and don't take up residence. An extension of this is to try and sterilise the resident animals so that in addition to not breeding, they also exclude other foxes from the area. This kind of thing has been tried with a number of species by putting hormones in bait but it has never been very successful. A more recent development still under trial is to find a virus that infects the species and insert proteins from the animal's reproductive system, such as those on the outer surface of the egg or the sperm, into the virus's coat. When the animal becomes infected the proteins cause the animal to immunise itself against its own reproduction and make it sterile. This is currently being attempted for foxes and rabbits. There is no guarantee that it will work and many people are suspicious about releasing modified viruses into the environment in case they do unpredictable things.

For those who regularly control foxes most of the above will seem like pie in the sky. This is partly because many of these techniques have not been fully tested to see whether they work or not. They have to compete with attitudes of gamekeepering and shepherding that have been around for several hundred years. Most people who kill animals on a regular basis regard it as a job just like any other, something that has no moral connotation. Obviously nowadays they are in a minority and subject to the opinions of the majority. However it is very easy to become desensitized to something through familiarity and if many aspects of country life, particularly field sports, are to survive then they have to be seen to be dealing seriously with matters like predator control and the humaneness or even the necessity of the different methods of killing animals.

Fox bites fox bites cat bites dog ...

A few years ago no book on foxes would have been complete without a chapter on rabies. In a few years time it may just be there as a footnote. The disease has always been about somewhere or other and is typically found in the commonest carnivores in each region of the world – feral dogs in the Middle East and South-east Asia, jackals in Africa, Arctic foxes in Siberia, raccoons and skunks in parts of the USA, mongeese in Grenada. The rabies epizootic (the same thing as an epidemic except it occurs in animals) that is of concern to this country at the moment first appeared in foxes in Poland between 1939 and 1945 and has been gradually moving westward through the European fox population ever since. It had reached Belgium by 1966 and France in 1968, and there were rabid foxes around Dieppe in 1990, next to the English Channel. The European virus is adapted to living in foxes but is quite capable of being passed on to other species and there have been cases reported in most carnivores. Virus particles reproduce in the nervous system and then accumulate in an infected animal's saliva, and the disease is generally transmitted by a bite. The likelihood of this is reinforced because a proportion of rabid foxes go through a 'furious' stage in which they will make unprovoked attacks on anything that moves near to them. This leads to non-carnivorous animals also being infected. The commonest of these are cattle, presumably because they are inquisitive and go and look at any foxes that are wandering about in the daytime and behaving peculiarly. There is a potential chain of transmission to domestic dogs and people. This is most commonly by way of cats which are more likely to come into contact with foxes, and which become furious more frequently than most species once they get the disease. In fact the number of people who have died of rabies contracted in Europe over the past fifty years can be counted on the fingers of one hand. However this has only been because many millions of marks, francs, etc, have been spent on vaccination, post exposure treatment and fox control in the countries affected.

For many years a lot of effort was put into trying to control rabies by killing foxes. While this may have had local effects on the frequency of cases it was completely ineffective in preventing the spread of the disease across the Continent. Intensive poisoning across the Jutland Peninsula prevented rabies getting into Denmark, but control by shooting foxes and gassing earths at a lower intensity could not achieve a sufficient level of population reduction across a disease front up to a thousand miles long from the Netherlands to Italy. In the 1970s there was a radical change in philosophy and practice, and attempts were made to vaccinate foxes so as to leave a stable population that was resistant to the disease. If you want to do this it's a bit difficult to catch all the foxes and inject them, but the next best thing is to leave baits lying about with vaccine in them so that foxes eat them and become immune. This is more difficult than it might at first seem; it is a lot easier to get an active vaccine into an animal by injecting it into its bloodstream than it is by feeding it, since the material has to survive digestion. A vaccine is basically something that has enough of the disease causing agent in it (in this case a virus) to enable the body's immune sytem to recognise it and manufacture proteins (antibodies) that bind to the invading body and disable it, while at the same time not having it in a condition that will actually cause the disease. Vaccines can be produced in several different ways.

The first rabies vaccine was produced by Louis Pasteur in 1884. He made it by infecting rabbits with the disease, killing them and removing their spinal cord, drying it and grinding it up, and then injecting it into other rabbits. After repeating this a lot of times the virus is gradually weakened. This kind of procedure is still carried out but nowadays duck eggs or cell cultures are used instead of rabbits. The resulting virus is still alive and can invade cells and force them to make more copies of it, but it is possible

Rabid fox.

for such vaccines to revert to their original disease-causing form. One way round this is to kill the virus completely by treating it with a chemical that wrecks its internal machinery but this also make it a poorer vaccine. The original oral vaccines used to treat wild foxes were modified live virus in capsules that had been stapled to chicken heads. This was first started in Switzerland in 1978 and turned out to be very successful. The country is divided up into compartments by long mountain ranges which restrict fox movement so that each valley could be treated in turn. The disease was almost eliminated but kept coming back over the borders from Germany, France and Austria. Other countries took up the idea and since European co-operation was fashionable at the time, they all made different vaccines and bait systems, and used them without any regard to what their neighbours were doing.

Another way of making a vaccine is to take a fully functioning virus and use modern genetic engineering techniques to change it so that chemically it looks like a rabies virus but is incapable of causing rabies. There are two ways of doing this. One is to take a completely different common virus that is mildly infectious but doesn't cause any serious diseases and insert genes from a rabies virus into it so that once it infects an animal the host thinks it is a rabies virus. The main vehicle for this is one of the cowpox family. The second is to take a real rabies virus and change a couple of its genes so that it can't cause the disease any more – changing one gene would be too risky as there is a danger of it reverting back to real rabies. When these vaccines were first produced people were worried about releasing engineered viruses into the environment, but there have been a number of trials in different parts of the world and nobody has come across any problems. Both types have been used in Belgium and France. There is now an EEC organised and funded programme for co-ordinated oral vaccination of foxes in western Europe which seems to be having a significant effect on outbreaks of the disease. In the first quarter of 1990 there were 930 cases of rabies identified in foxes in France. By the first quarter of 1995 this had dropped to 13 and the rabies front had retreated several hundred kilometres from the Channel coast. There are still a few foci of infection in Belgium and Germany and it will be a several years before it is certain that rabies is under control. In addition there remains the problem of eastern Europe where these expensive techniques are more difficult to apply, but there is a prospect that rabies may be eliminated from most of Europe in the foreseeable future.

Muzzling, leashing and poisoning

Rabies used to occur in Britain but it was mainly in stray dogs. During the 19th century various laws were introduced to allow such dogs to be rounded up and to enforce the muzzling of any pet dogs that were taken out on the streets. By the first decade of this century rabies had disappeared. There was a brief reinfestation at the end of the First World War, but since then the country has been free of the disease. There is little firm evidence that rabies was present in wildlife at any time. Packs of fox hounds had occasionally to be put down because they had developed the disease. In 1819 the Duke of Richmond is supposed to have died of rabies after cutting himself shaving and being licked on the face by his tame fox. Many people died after being bitten by various animals but this could be for a number of reasons. Before the development of antibiotics anybody contracting septicaemia from even a slight puncture wound was liable to end up raving and expiring in a high fever. Nowadays rabies is diagnosed by a battery of laboratory techniques, but in the past the only definite symptom was a violent reaction to water (hydrophobia) which doesn't always occur. Fox populations were probably not dense enough to support rabies. There are reports of them having other diseases such as mange, but these were probably due to the number of bag and put down foxes that were used for hunting. These would spend varying periods in sacks, boxes and kennels where they could pick up a range of things, rabies included. There are now far more foxes in the countryside and also in the suburbs of cities so there is a danger that wildlife rabies could take hold if it were introduced.

Since we live on an island, quarantine and, if that failed, slaughter of infected animals has always seemed the best option to politicians and veterinarians in the face of a dangerous disease. For many years there has been a contingency plan for wildlife rabies control in Britain which involves burying thousands of poison baits in an infected area to try and kill off all the foxes. Initially the poison to be used was strychnine which is very stable. The successor to that is a nerve poison developed at Porton Down which decomposes after a few days at normal temperatures so that even if baits can't be recovered afterwards they will not remain toxic. Up until recently the use of oral vaccination was disregarded because the main

types available still used live virus, and there was a fear that this might start another rabies outbreak instead of controlling the first. With more modern vaccines this should not be a problem. Laying large amounts of poison about in the countryside would have collateral effects on other wildlife which nobody has seriously tried to predict, on the grounds that rabies is such a horrific disease that any measures for its eradication can be justified. When we become more integrated into Europe, there will be pressure to harmonise our animal health laws with those in the EEC. Quarantine, which has already been modified, could be phased out (although it will always remain for animals from outside Europe) and replaced by the vaccination and licensing of pets.

Fox odds and ends

Foxgloves Common wild and garden flowers, properly known as *Digitalis purpurea*. They are most notable for their production of 'digitalin' which is one of the main drugs used in the treatment of heart problems. The plants were important at one time in folk medicine. Taken internally they are a strong diuretic and were used to release fluid from the body in conditions such as dropsy. Externally they were used as a poultice to help the healing of wounds. They are also an antidote to aconite poisoning. If consumed in any quantity the plants are poisonous themselves. One of the symptoms of poisoning is the seeing of yellow halos around objects. It has been suggested that Vincent Van Gogh was treated with extract of foxgloves by his physician, Dr Gachet, and that this affected his late painting style. The main evidence for this is a couple of portraits of Gachet showing foxgloves standing in a glass on his desk. There is some debate about the origin of the common name. Some say it is a corruption of the phrase 'folk's glove' referring, presumably, to 'The Little People'. If this is so then it should have been called Folk's Mittens. The size and shape of the flower are not inconsistent with its being able to fit over a fox's foot. However, do not try this at home!

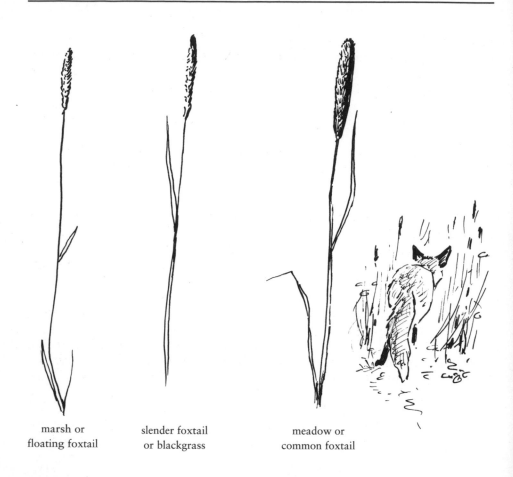

marsh or
floating foxtail

slender foxtail
or blackgrass

meadow or
common foxtail

Fox bane One of the names for the yellow flowered *Aconitum vulparia*, a Central European relative of the better known blue Monk's Hood and Wolf's Bane. Despite being popular in gardens these are among the most poisonous plants growing in Europe. The name comes from the fact that at one time extract of the roots was used for poisoning arrow heads for shooting wolves and foxes (among other things). This is no longer recommended as a method of fox control.

Fox poison A local English name for the spurge laurel, *Daphne laureola*. This contains a number of poisonous compounds, particularly in the berries. However the name is probably more of an *aide-memoire* than a description.

Foxtails   The purple loosestrife, *Lythrum salicaria*, so-called because of its long, tapering flower spike. This is a plant that was studied in detail by Charles Darwin because it has three different types of flowers, all with different size sexual parts, and eighteen possible modes of pollination!

Fox stones   While we're on the subject of sexual parts, this is another name for the early purple orchid, *Orchis mascula*. It has two large, ovoid tubers which those with an eye for that kind of thing have likened to fox's testicles. These could prove a useful alternative for any fox hunters who want to imitate the traditions of Spanish bull fighters (although possibly with the same effects, as the plant was once used by witches who thought that the appearance would make it a good aphrodisiac). The Arabic for fox's testicles, *Khusa-al-thalab*, became *Salhab* in Turkish, which was the name for a herbal drink made from orchid roots. This was popular in England during the 18th century. One of the anglicised forms of this was 'Salep'. This is close to the word 'Salop', an alternative name for Shropshire. Some people, such as the essayist Charles Lamb, associated the two, although it is doubtful whether Salopians appreciated this (in either sense).

Fox's brush   Another name for red valerian, *Centrathus ruber*, a popular garden plant, occasionally used in salads. Extract of valerian roots is supposed to be attractive to cats, foxes and rats and has been used as a scent lure for trapping.

Foxberry   An alternative name for the cowberry, *Vaccinium vitis-idaea*. Bit difficult to confuse a fox and a cow, but maybe somebody left their glasses at home.

Fox-rose   *Rosa spinosissima*, more commonly known as the burnet or Scotch rose, and not to be confused with the dog rose.

Fox and cubs   A flower, *Hieracium aurantiacum* (also known as orange hawkweed or grim-the-collier) which has escaped from gardens. It looks a bit, but not totally like a dandelion. Unfortunately it is related to several hundred similar species which all look a bit, but not totally like dandelions. This is because of their peculiar reproductive practices (information on these can be obtained from your local University Botany Department under plain cover).

Fox and hounds   A local English name for the toadflax, *Linaria vulgaris*, a wild relative of the snapdragon, so called because the flowers are a mixture of orange and yellow.

Foxtail grasses   Grasses of the genus *Alopecurus*. There are six species in Britain. Two of the commonest have elongated flower heads which look like a fox's brush. Some of the rarer species look more like bottle brushes, but by the time grassologists had discovered these they were stuck with the name.

Fox sedge   A small, spiky, grasslike plant with the Latin name of *Carex vulpina*. This looks nothing like any part of the anatomy of a fox but the flower head is slightly red in colour (or at least Linnaeus thought so). On no account should it be confused with the false fox sedge, *Carex otrubae*, which looks absolutely nothing like a fox whatsoever.

Fox moth   A large, dumpy reddish brown moth, *Macrothylacia rubi*, related to the lackeys and eggars (other large,dumpy reddish brown moths). Not related to the tiger moth.

False fox sedge.

Fox   An old English sword, so called because of the Spanish maker's mark on the blade. This was actually meant to be a small dog, but was misinterpreted as a fox. Thus we can correct Shakespeare:

> O Signieur Dew, thou diest on point of poodle,
> Except, O Signieur, thou do give to me
> Egregious ransom.
>
> *Henry V*, Act IV, scene iv

Foxing   The nasty brown stains that appear on some kinds of paper (not the stuff that comes in rolls). It occurs on old books and prints that have been stored in damp conditions and is probably due to a combination of fungal growth and the mobilisation of iron salts in the acidified paper.

Foxy spot   A name for a medium sized toadstool, *Collybia maculata*, with (you guessed it) brown spots.

Floating foxtail.

Fox-fire Decayed wood that has been penetrated by some kinds of fungus glows in the dark, as a result of chemical reactions in the fungal tissue (called bioluminescence). So if you go out at night and see a glowing stump, it is not evil forces at work (unless somebody's set light to your garden).

Fox's wedding A sudden splattering of raindrops which appear out of a clear sky. There is a country belief that when this happens, somewhere a fox is getting married! (I know it sounds like A. A. Milne on a bad day, but my granny swears it's true).

Fox and goose A board game where there are a lot of pieces representing geese and one big piece acting as the fox. The game ends when the geese have either boxed in the fox so that it can't move, or the fox has eaten all the geese by jumping over each of them into an empty space. Could also be a bawdy game where you outwit somebody and then creep up behind them (this is different from that other popular country game called Hunt the Squirrel).

Brushpiece

People and foxes have been associated for as long as there has been settled agriculture. The relationship has never been as intimate as with its
cousin the wolf, who (while we may have tried to exterminate the wild
species) we have integrated into society through its descendant, the domestic dog. The fox has always had a more peripheral position. If you
look at the diet of foxes in Britain today, most of it is a by-product of
human activity. Rabbits were introduced into the country for meat and
fur and are now an agricultural pest. Voles are much more numerous in
some places than they would otherwise be as a result of commercial forestry. Sheep and deer now inhabit large parts of the country where there
were once unaltered forests and bogs. Game birds are artificially main-
tained at much higher densities than would occur naturally. And this
doesn't even start to include foxes living in the suburbs of cities. The fox
is not dependant on human activities in the sense that it would disappear
without them, but it would be a lot less common if they went away. In
the past the fox had a fairly settled position in society. It was either pest
or quarry and was treated accordingly. Nowadays its situation is more
complex and it is caught up in many of the current conflicts over agricul-

tural practices, field sports, conservation and animal welfare. What is its role going to be in the future?

Many people argue that the fox's activities in the countryside are, on balance, beneficial. To take one important example we can consider predation on rabbits. Having recovered from the effects of myxomatosis rabbit populations have re-emerged in some parts of the country to become a serious agricultural problem again. This has mainly occurred in the eastern half of Britain. In the west rabbits still seem to be much rarer than they were before myxomatosis was introduced. There could be a number of reasons for this, but one suggestion is that with the increased amount of afforestation and less predator control, the rabbits are being kept down by foxes and other carnivores. One recent theory on predator-prey relationships suggests that an animal such as a fox can suppress a rabbit population and keep it at a low level provided the rabbits never get above a certain threshold. However once the rabbits go beyond this, due to some third factor, then they swamp the foxes and carry on increasing until they hit another threshold, like the food supply. Intensive predator control by gamekeepers in the last century has always been suggested as one of the reasons why the rabbit became established as a pest. Rabbits are also demonstrably more numerous on keepered shooting estates than they are in places where there is no killing of predators. You have to try and consider what would happen if foxes and rabbits were just left to their own devices. While rabbit populations might be lower, the fox is an opportunist operator and there will be times of the year when it will find it easier to switch temporarily to another food supply, like ground-nesting birds. Your attitude to this is going to depend upon what you regard as most important: having more foxes, less rabbits or more birds. Obviously if they were left alone, fox populations would not go on increasing for ever. They have well documented processes of self regulation. Territorial behaviour spreads breeding animals across the available habitat. As numbers increase litter sizes become smaller. Younger foxes within the population fail to breed and either attach themselves to their family group in a subordinate role or try and disperse. These kind of 'saturation' conditions probably already operate in some rural fox populations and are common amongst urban foxes.

It would be nice to think that out there somewhere there is a natural world which can just be left alone to get on with its legitimate concerns and that the fox is part of it. Unfortunately, even if that ever were the case, it certainly isn't now. In our constantly shrinking globe nearly every part has been touched by some aspect of human activity. Preservation of the few remaining pristine habitats is going to require active management. How much more so must this apply to those parts of the landscape that we use for food production and recreation? Having been brought up as a good Darwinian, I have always held the view that our main concern should be to preserve as much variety and diversity as possible in the environment, both for our own interest and use, and to hand on. How to proceed with such management in any particular place is going to depend upon the local circumstances and objectives. When this comes to foxes there are going to be some situations where they can be left alone and others where strict control of some kind will be necessary. Simple theoretical or ideological views of the countryside are unlikely to provide the means for deciding this. The purpose of legislation in the environment as much as elsewhere should be for the restriction of excess rather than the imposition of conformity.

Much of the course of agriculture during this century has been towards the production of crop monocultures, promoted by treatment with fertilisers, herbicides and pesticides. This is a system dedicated to the reduction of diversity. The root of practical conservation, which tries to increase the diversity of animal and plant species, is habitat preservation and creation. Nature reserves, volunteer groups maintaining things like ponds and old railway lines, and government handouts to farmers to continue existing practices in Environmentally Sensitive Areas all have a part to play in this, but, combined, they only account for a fraction of the land area. Those who object to fox killing should not underestimate the role of game preservation and hunting in maintaining a more habitat-rich, working countryside which also sustains incomes and lifestyles for those living there. Of course it may be that some field sports, in terms of public sentiment, have reached their sell-by date, and, with sufficient will and research, it may be possible to replace existing methods of predator management with less destructive techniques. The danger is in isolating one issue, animal welfare, and using it to obscure all the other problems that need to be considered in a more holistic view of the countryside. Anyway, whatever anybody decides about the future of such things as sheep farming, fox hunting or game management there are still likely to be enough foxes to go round. Having scrounged off people for the last few thousand years, they know a good bet when they see one.

Further reading

H. G. Lloyd, *The Red Fox* (Batsford, London, 1980)

S. Harris, *Urban Foxes* (Whittet Books, London, 1986)

G. B. Corbet & S. Harris, *The Handbook of British Mammals* (3rd Ed) (Blackwell, Oxford, 1991)

D. W. Macdonald, *Rabies and Wildlife* (Oxford University Press, Oxford, 1980)

D.W. Macdonald, *Running with the Fox* (Unwin Hyman, London, 1988)

L. E. Bueler, *Wild Dogs of the World* (Constable, London, 1974)

R. Burrows, *Wild Fox* (David and Charles, Newton Abbot, 1968)

R. Page, *A Fox's Tale* (Hodder and Stoughton, London, 1986)

M. Clayton, *The Chase. A Modern Guide to Foxhunting* (Stanley Paul, London, 1987)

Index

*Page numbers in bold indicate illus-
trations*

Whittet Natural History

• Informative • Easy to read • Packed with facts
• Written by specialists in their subjects
• Suitable for all interested in wildlife, young enthusiasts and adults • Recommended by *BBC Wildlife magazine*, *Natural World magazine*, *New Scientist* and *School Librarian*, amongst many others

Three times Highly Commended in the Natural World book awards

'There is no equivalent for these highly accessible texts on animal groups.' - *The Countryman*

'The Whittet series on natural history have rapidly become well established as informal and informative books, relatively cheap and of dependable quality.' - *The Environmentalist*

If you have enjoyed this book, you might be interested to know of the other titles in the same series, all of which are written by experts, in the same style of easily accessible information. All titles in the British series are £7.99. You may order them direct from us,

Whittet Books Ltd
18 Anley Road
London W14 OBY

by adding £1.50 postage and packing. Visa or Mastercard can be accepted. Quote your card number and expiry date as well as full name and billing address.

The full list of titles available appears on the following pages.

World Wildlife Series

ANTS
Ray North

BIG CATS
Doug Richardson
(£9.99- this title includes colour photographs)

CHIMPANZEES
Tess Lemmon

DOLPHINS
Peter Evans

DUCKS
David Tomlinson

PARROTS
David Alderton (£9.99 - this title includes colour photographs)

PENGUINS
John A. Love

SEA OTTERS
John A. Love
(£9.99 - this title includes colour photographs)

SPIDERS
Michael Chinery